Lucy Shaw's
Not Sure

JO BAVINGTON-JONES

Lucy Shaw's Not Sure

2nd Edition Published by The Conrad Press in the United Kingdom 2020

1st Edition (ISBN 978-1-911546-24-5) Published by The Conrad Press in 2017

Tel: +44(0)1227 472 874

www.theconradpress.com

info@theconradpress.com

ISBN 978-1-913567-12-5

Book cover design and typesetting by:

Charlotte Mouncey, www.bookstyle.co.uk

The Conrad Press logo was designed by Maria Priestley

Printed and bound in Great Britain by Clays Ltd, Elcograf S.p.A..

For Sam, my raison d'être.

1

just like starting over

My decree absolute arrived with that morning's post. *No more Mr. Nisi guy*. I sighed. My marriage was absolutely over. I was thirty-four years old, had been separated from my husband for two years, and was now finally, completely divorced.

So, here I was, Lucy Shaw, all five feet eight inches of me, long legs poking out of the white cotton grandad shirt I sometimes wore in bed, golden-brown hair, still ruffled from my pillow, hanging in waves down my back, and green eyes still full of sleep. A bit different from sensible-suited Monday-to-Friday Lucy Shaw, who worked in the accounts department at Horizon Pharmaceuticals.

I really wasn't sure how I felt about my divorce becoming final. Relieved? Yes, I was relieved to have some sort of closure. But it was also one of the saddest moments of my life. My marriage had failed. I had failed. I didn't want to feel down – I usually avoided it with a joke or a ready smile for whoever was around at the time. I didn't want to think about, or be reminded of, things that made me sad, and this legal document in front of me forced me to confront feelings of failure I preferred to keep buried.

I didn't know whether to round up my girlfriends for a vodka-soaked night on the tiles, or take to my bed with a DVD, a big box of chocolates and an even bigger box of tissues. So it was, feeling decidedly glum and emotionally muddled, that I plodded through to the kitchen where my housemate, Carrie, was making tea.

'Well, it's official. I'm a divorcee,' I said. It had been over two years since my marriage broke down due to 'irreconcilable differences' – irreconcilable similarities would have been more accurate if you asked me as the dislike was mutual at the time. The incompatibility that I had refused to see for a long time, had eventually turned to dislike.

'Oh, Lucy, I'm sorry. I do know how it feels – I've been there, remember,' Carrie replied softly as she ran her fingers through her spiky blonde morning-hair. Carrie was older than me at forty-one and had two grown-up children. Her son had moved into his own place and her daughter had just gone off to university, leaving Carrie alone in the house and looking for, not only company, but a little extra income too. Carrie had a rather disastrous track record with men, and was slow to trust any new man who came on the scene. Petite next to me, but equally full of fun, Carrie and I had hit it off straight away. She did have an air of fragile sadness about her, but she always put her happy face on for the world.

Carrie hugged me and handed me a cup of tea. We went to sit on the sofa in the lounge together, part of our Saturday morning routine, where tulips drooped colourful heads in a vase on the fireplace and the April sunshine filtered into the room through the voile at the window. Carrie's little house in Maidstone always had fresh flowers, and the drooping heads of the slightly sad-looking tulips suited my mood.

'I don't know why I feel so sad after all this time,' I sighed.

'I've never regretted the split for a minute. I suppose it just makes it so final, so official. I guess I feel like a failure. For a change. Starting over at the age of thirty-four.'

'Lucy Shaw, you are NOT a failure! You're a funny, clever, warm and beautiful woman. Rob simply wasn't right for you. One day you'll find Mr. Right. In the meantime, just enjoy a few Mr. Right Nows!'

I laughed, but rather half-heartedly.

Why were other people so sure of me? I wondered. I may have been Lucy Shaw by name, but certainly not by nature. All I wanted out of life was to find something, or someone, that would bring me lasting happiness and contentment. I currently had no idea what that might be.

And that was the whole point. Yes, my name was Lucy Shaw, but I wasn't sure what would make me happy. I hadn't got a clue, to be honest. That bright April morning, with my dear friend Carrie, at number 5 Victoria Close, a pretty little cul-de-sac on the south side of Maidstone, and with my decree absolute on the dining table in front of me, I was feeling more than a little lost.

I smiled at Carrie ruefully. 'I'm sorry. I'm just being pathetic. Take no notice. I'll be fine.'

'You're not being pathetic, you're being human, silly! You're allowed to feel sad and confused – you were with Rob for half your life. Those feelings don't just disappear.'

'I know. You're right. As ever! I'm just surprised to feel this sad after all this time.'

'Someone once told me that the end of a marriage is like a death - you have to go through all the different stages of mourning before you can really accept it and move on. It takes as long as it takes. There aren't any rules.'

'In that case, I think I just visited the grave and laid a final posy of flowers,' I sighed.

'You'll be fine, Lucy. I just know that wonderful things will come your way.'

'I wish I had your confidence. Besides, I'm not sure I'd recognise something wonderful if it jumped out and shouted "I'm your something wonderful, Lucy Shaw," at the top of its voice, whilst slapping me round the face with a wet fish.'

Carrie laughed. 'Of course you would, you doughnut.'

'I'm not so sure,' I replied with yet another sigh. 'I think maybe Rob was right about me.'

'What d'you mean? Right about what?' Carrie asked as she put her now empty mug on the table and wriggled back down into the cushions, tucking her legs under her, and turning more towards me.

Echoing Carrie's body language, I too curled my legs up and twisted my body to face her directly.

'Well,' I began, 'when Rob and I first split, he said that I'd never be happy. That if he couldn't make me happy, loving me as much as he did, then no-one would be able to. He said I didn't know how to accept someone's love and never would. That I was damaged goods – a product of a broken home, destined to repeat the mistakes of my parents.' A silent tear rolled down my cheek as I spoke. I had never told anyone this before.

'I'm sure he was just lashing out – trying to make you feel bad, because he was hurting. He didn't mean it,' Carrie said as she gently wiped the tear away with her thumb.

'I told myself that at the time, but now I'm not so sure. What if he was right, Carrie? What if I don't know how to be happy? How to love and be loved? What if I'm destined for nothing but one failed relationship after another? I couldn't bear it!'

'Oh, Lucy. I don't believe that for a second. You're one of the most loving and caring people I know. You were so young when you met Rob – too young – you can't base the rest of your life on the failure of that one relationship.'

'God, I hope you're right, Carrie, but whenever something happens in my life, or I meet someone new, Rob's words come back to taunt me. It scares me. Everything scares me.'

'Oh dear! What can I do to cheer you up?' Carrie asked, recognising that she needed to try and snap me out of the blue mood that was threatening. 'Do you want to hit the town tonight? We could drink and dance off your blues. Vodka and Motown cures all known ailments!' Carrie loved Motown music and it always lifted her mood no end. Carrie sometimes got a little down at weekends, without the busyness of her job as a legal secretary to keep her mind occupied, and away from the sadness of her own failed marriage.

'Thanks, Carrie, but I don't think I'll be in the mood. I'll see how I feel later.' Ultimately, the final and official failure of my marriage was not something I wanted to celebrate. 'I think I'm just going to go back to bed and wallow for a while.' I hugged Carrie and headed back down the cellar stairs to what was now my room, but had formerly belonged to Carrie's daughter. The cool darkness of the underground room seemed a fitting atmosphere for wallowing. Well, it was a Saturday morning, thank goodness, so I didn't need to go to work and I could just indulge my self-pity.

Putting on my snuggliest PJs, and armed with a big box of

Maltesers I had stashed for an emergency such as this, I crawled back under the duvet and settled down to watch *City of Angels*, which always reduced me to tears when Meg Ryan's character dies. Great choice of film, Lucy. What about watching *Love Story* next?

Ninety minutes or so later I was surrounded by snotty, tear-sodden Kleenex and my face was suitably red and puffy. I also had a thumping headache and felt slightly nauseous after consuming so much chocolate. I guess the end result would have been pretty much the same if I'd taken the alternative course of action, and gone out drinking. Why was it that crying always gave me such a terrible headache? People always say *Have a good cry, you'll feel so much better.* 'No I bloody won't. I'll feel like death warmed up, and look like a blotchy frog.'

I wondered if Rob, my now ex-husband, had also received his decree that morning and if he was feeling the same as me. I could picture him in the house we'd shared, sitting at the kitchen table with the letter open in front of him, and our dog Jasper's head resting on his thigh, brown eyes turned up to Rob's face, trying to offer him comfort. I hoped he was OK. I would always care about the man who had been my first love. In spite of his harsh words when we'd split.

I was just sixteen when we met, Rob was eighteen, and he was my first serious boyfriend. He wasn't overly tall and not a particularly handsome man, but he made me laugh and, more importantly, he made me feel safe and loved. We got married when I was twenty-one, and had the whole 'white wedding' thing and I would never forget the pride on his face and his blue eyes shining as I walked up the aisle towards him. Deep down I think I knew, as I made that walk, that I was doing the wrong thing, but I wasn't sure, and I could never have left Rob standing at the altar anyway.

The problem was, as I only realised some years into the marriage, that I had fallen in love with the idea of being in love and not really with Rob himself. Coming from a broken home as I did, I thought that all I wanted was to be with someone who would never let me down. And Rob never did. But he also didn't let me grow and flourish as a person; he wrapped me up in cotton wool and stood me on a pedestal, doing everything for me, and protecting me from the big bad world. He'd never let me put petrol in my car, and always drove if we went out together. When I had tried to assert myself within the relationship, he somehow managed to make me feel that my efforts weren't quite good enough and that it was better to let him take care of everything. It was easier to let him get on with it than to rock the boat of our relationship. Over time, though, I felt more and more stifled and came to resent Rob and to see him as controlling. I suppose those festering feelings of resentment destroyed whatever love I had for him.

My guess was that, on receipt of the divorce papers, Rob would have taken our golden retriever, Jasper, for a long, long walk and spent some time quietly contemplating his lost love and what an absolute bitch I was for ending our eleven-year marriage. It had been hard leaving Jasper with Rob, but as Rob was staying in the marital home, and I wasn't sure exactly what my living arrangements would be, I felt I had no choice. And Rob adored Jasper. I think he might have fallen apart without him. Having a dog, like having a child, gives you a reason to get out of bed every morning, whether you feel like it or not.

The trouble was I did feel like an absolute bitch at times.

I didn't know if the guilt would ever go away. Rob and I had been teenage sweethearts and after four years he had proposed to me. We were together for sixteen, not unhappy but rather unfulfilling, years. I had grown *older* within the relationship but I hadn't really grown *up*. I had let Rob take care of everything. To the extent that when we split up I had indeed never even put petrol in my car.

And so when we separated, two years earlier, I was thirty-two years old and absolutely pathetic. I'd been terrified of what lay ahead and had no idea how I was going to manage, but I was also exhilarated and excited at the prospect of venturing out into the big wide world on my own. I'd known deep down I'd done the right thing. I just wish I hadn't had to hurt someone I would always care very deeply about in the process. My beautiful Jasper. I felt bad about hurting Rob too of course. (Oh, ha ha, Lucy. Why did I always feel the need to hide the hurt behind a great chunk of funny? I wondered. I absolutely hated myself for hurting Rob and just hoped that he could forgive me more easily than I could forgive myself.)

Feeling the emotional equivalent of a wrung-out dishcloth, I drifted into a deep, dreamless sleep…

2

Later that day

I woke up at about tea-time that same day, still feeling a little sad but surprisingly refreshed, and no longer so much in need of sympathy. Just tea. I hurried up the stairs in search of Carrie and found her painting her nails a vivid shade of red.

'Fancy a cuppa, Carrie? Or shall we move straight on to the vodka?!'

Carrie laughed. 'Glad to see you're feeling better.'

'Yes, I'm happy to say I am. Could we have that night out after all? Well, it's a girl's prerogative to change her mind.'

'Absolutely! I could do with letting my hair down after the week I've had at work.'

'Yay! Thank you, lovely lady! I'm so glad I've got you!'

'No need to thank me. What are friends for after all? Now, do you want me to paint your nails?'

'Yes, in *Scarlet Woman* please,' knowing full well that was the colour she was applying.

Sitting in companionable silence while our nails dried, my thoughts drifted back to six months earlier when I'd first met Carrie. I'd answered her 'room to let' ad and had the good sense to choose Carrie's place over the one with a 'large, airy room overlooking established gardens' in a 'spacious and well-appointed house'. They neglected to mention that the occupants all locked their bedroom doors and that the house was about as welcoming as Rob's mum when she heard about our split. Carrie's house might have been small, and my room might have had more than a little resemblance to a dungeon, but it was home. I never felt like a lodger in Carrie's house.

'Right! Time to go and make myself look beautiful!' I announced, coming out of my reverie.

'You always look beautiful, Lucy.'

'Aw! Thanks! I'm just trying to keep up with you!' Blowing Carrie a kiss, and before the mutual appreciation society got chundersome, I took myself back downstairs to get ready.

Listening to music was always part of getting ready for a night out. The right music got you in the right mood. That or the vodka, anyway. My music of choice was *Club Classics* as they made me want to dance and I boogied around my bedroom as I thought about what to wear. I was trying to be as upbeat as the music, but sad thoughts connected to Rob and our relationship kept sneaking up on me. We'd often talked about having children, but we'd never wanted a child at the same time. Rob had seemed happy enough with that, but I was always conscious of my biological clock ticking. Suddenly I heard it tick now, and with an insistent loudness. I went to turn the music up, as if to drown out the sound.

Ever since my thirtieth birthday, I'd been having to turn up music more and more to smother the increasingly pregnant tick, tock, TICK, TOCK. It just wasn't working! If only I could take the batteries out. I'd already tried smothering the thing with chocolate chip cookies to no avail. *Maybe I could drown the bugger in vodka,* I thought, taking a swig.

Hoping to paint the town red, I knew I'd probably have to settle for more of a rosy glow. I'd never been much of a drinker, though I began drinking more when Rob and I were separated, but even now I tended only to consume enough to give me the courage to go and dance. I loved dancing. I had no idea if I was really any good, but I regretted all my sober years when I was too inhibited to dance in public.

Finally deciding on what to wear, I squeezed into my denim cat-suit, slipped my feet into some killer heels, a final squirt of perfume, a last look in the mirror to check my make-up and I was ready to go. My feet were objecting even by the time I reached the top of the cellar stairs, but I knew that the vodka would soon reach them and they'd be nicely anaesthetised. I'd be able to walk home quite happily at 2 a.m. after hours of shaking my booty at Raspberry Fools nightclub. It would only be when I took off my sandals before tackling the stairs to the cellar that I would realise the straps had gouged holes in my little toes and I had several impressive blisters. Still, I'd know better next time. Yeah right!

Carrie was looking as fabulous as ever with her slim figure and spiky blonde hair. She may have had two grown-up children but she still looked amazing. We were quite a contrast with me being a tall brunette with rather ample… er… shall we say assets? I felt as though I'd been friends with Carrie forever and we always had such good times together. We poured ourselves another drink: vodka and lemonade for me (I still didn't really like the taste of alcohol) and vodka and tonic for Carrie.

Time for the next part of our Saturday night ritual: watching a talent show for singers. There were a couple of guys on it we both adored and I had a huge crush on one particular singer who was the epitome of tall, dark and handsome. Danny Campbell: my ideal man. When he sang 'Second Look', I knew that he was really singing it to me. Yeah, in my dreams! We may have been two supposedly quite *mature* women (pause for side-splitting laughter and a spray of vodka) but we were not above drooling over pop wannabes and cackling about 'moist gussets'!

Then it was time to head off to our first watering hole, a High Street pub with cheap drinks aplenty and the right kind of pre-party atmosphere. We were old enough to have given birth to most of the other patrons of this particular establishment, but we could more than hold our own. Could probably hold our drink better too.

It was a beautiful spring evening and the twenty-minute, mainly downhill, walk into town passed in a whirl of giggling and chatting. Before we knew it we had arrived at a Wetherspoons. There were bouncers on the door, checking IDs. Perish the thought that any underage drinkers should gain entry to the premises. Maybe they only looked about thirteen to us. For some unfathomable reason we were not asked for ID, just ushered through the door to join the seething mass of bodies queuing at the bar.

I think one of the reasons it was so cheap to drink at Wetherspoons was because it took so long to get served that you didn't have time for too many drinks before it was time to head off to your next destination. We finally reached the front line and started jostling for position at the bar. That was where it could come in handy being not only a woman, but a buxom one at that, unless the bar tender also was. Eventually, drinks purchased, we did a bit of people watching. Wetherspoons was a great place for this as it had an upstairs balcony where you could get an eagle-eye view of the meat market taking place below. We headed up there and passed the time doing a David Attenborough-style commentary on the mating rituals taking place below.

'Here we see a prime example of the male of the species, the Greater-Spotted Pimple Bird, doing his best to attract a mate,' I said in my best bird-spotter voice.

'Watch as he struts over to his chosen female, trying to look cool as he slicks his hand through his hair,' Carrie giggled.

'The female feigns disinterest, flicking her long blonde hair back and turning away. She's clearly playing hard to get – the male will have to pull out all the stops.'

'Undeterred, the male circles her and attempts to make eye contact. He smiles his sexiest smile. Oh dear! He may have blown it! That wasn't sexy at all.'

'But the female is giggling now, sucking provocatively on the straw in her bright red cocktail. She's clearly interested.'

'Or desperate!' Carrie and I announced simultaneously. We were so on the same wavelength.

Clinking our glasses together, we laughed and toasted the couple we'd been watching. They were actually kind of sweet, and I think I did sigh a little enviously. That first connection with someone was such a rush. I wanted to feel it again.

10 p.m. arrived and it was time to move on to Raspberry Fools. I suppose you'd call it a nightclub, but really it was a pub with a dance floor and plenty of cheesy music. You could guarantee they'd play S Club 7 and Steps at least once during the night which were right up our dance street. And, better still, it was full of men. Wonderful, gullible and oh-so-predictable, men!

By day, Carrie was a legal secretary and I worked in accounts.

But on a night out, Carrie became a solicitor (of the legal variety) and I was transformed into a sex therapist. We had supposedly met when she referred couples to me for counselling. The scam was that while I liked to keep my risqué-sounding job to myself for fear of unwanted attention, Carrie would divulge my secret to a few simple souls. Men that is. The effect was instant and predictable. Just hearing the word 'sex' made them instantly attracted to me. Poor sad creatures. I suppose it wasn't really their fault. It's just the way they're programmed.

This night was no different. One minute I'm dancing away, minding my own business, and reaching for the stars along with the best of them, when a guy comes over and shouts in my ear: 'Even if I hadn't known what you did for a living, I could have told by the way you dance.' Clearly Carrie had whispered in his ear that I was a sex therapist.

'Oh my God,' I screamed, 'I dance like an accountant!' Poor sod, he didn't stand a chance. Maybe the person who named the club knew what they were doing!

I could also count on at least one bloke coming up to me during the evening and asking if my boobs were real. He also asked two other entirely predictable questions. I was seriously considering getting a T-shirt printed with:

Yes
32HH
No you can't

As with any club, Raspberry Fools made Smithfield Market look positively vegan. Men and women displayed their wares for potential buyers. But for Carrie and me it was all about window shopping. We weren't particularly interested in the best bit of rump or a nice sausage. I'm not saying we were vegetarian. Far from it. But for us it was the thrill of the hunt, rather than the kill at the end. We would go home alone, with our feet sore but our egos nicely massaged.

3

Letting go and moving on

I tried not to dwell on my divorce in the three or four weeks that followed. After separating, Rob and I hadn't been in any hurry to get divorced and had waited the required two years before filing the papers. I thought about him often though and hoped he was happy. (But not so happy that he didn't think of me from time to time of course. I may have moved out but I hadn't moved on. I couldn't quite let go of my ex, and while I didn't want him anymore, I sure as hell didn't want him to want anyone else. Screwy huh? But, as you will discover, that's me in a nutshell.)

Anyway, I vowed not to make the same mistakes again. What I didn't realise was how many new ones I'd be making. So, there I was, thirty-four years old and sowing some very belated wild oats. To be honest I was never going to need a combine harvester, but I might be able to manage a small bowl of porridge when it came to harvest time. I was definitely a late starter, but now I was off the bench and playing the field nicely, thank you. My confidence grew over time and I was even going to the petrol station unaccompanied. (I had to take a friend with me for ages because I was too scared to do it on my own. What if I couldn't get the petrol cap off/on? What if someone rang my mobile and the whole place exploded? etc.)

With this new-found confidence came new opportunities

at work too and, about the middle of May, I was head-hunted by a very successful American company with offices in the UK, including one in Maidstone. Life was good. Shame my new boss turned out to be a complete prat. Still, I was earning enough to support myself and have a decent social life so I couldn't really complain.

Although I did, of course. To anyone who would listen. Luckily the consensus of opinion within the building was that the Head of Accounts was indeed a prize pillock. We were united in our loathing of the man and this made life bearable. Every time he uttered his favourite adage, 'I'm not here to win a popularity contest' (silly sod hadn't even filled out an entry form) we all sniggered behind our screens or did the eyebrow-raising equivalent of a Mexican wave around the office.

It had been when I went for the second interview for this particular job that I discovered love at first sight. I think it must have been love and not lust at first sight because the man under whose spell I had fallen worked in manufacturing and was wearing a most unattractive hairnet at the time. When he took off this delightful head adornment as I was intro-duced to him, my fate was sealed. He was absolutely gorgeous. Tall, well-built without being too muscly, and with a mane of almost auburn-coloured hair. Not quite brown but definitely not ginger either. I mentally thanked my lucky stars that I was looking my best in a flattering trouser suit, with my shoul-der-length hair glossy and styled and a little natural make-up applied to my now undoubtedly flushed face. When he spoke I discovered he had a soft Liverpudlian accent which made me go weak at the knees. And other places. His name was Dan.

Liverpool's loss was definitely Maidstone's gain. This man was premier league.

I think I did manage to say something vaguely comprehensible after I had picked my jaw up off the floor. And I certainly gave him my sexiest smile. At least I hoped it was sexy. It may just have been salacious. I decided there and then that I would accept the position if it was offered to me. Who knew what other interesting positions it might lead to?

I did get the job. Unfortunately, it wasn't long before I found out that Dan had a fairly long-term girlfriend. You can imagine how gutted I was. Jane wasn't much of a looker, with her short, mousy-brown hair and glasses, but I liked her. She was quiet and softly spoken, and was always friendly towards me. The lucky bitch. If she'd been stunning I would probably have hated her guts. Shallow? Me? I'll have you know I'm as deep as a teaspoon. I knew I would just have to admire Dan from afar and accept that we were not to be. I told myself I was enjoying the single life too much and had no desire to embark on anything too serious in the relationship stakes. Trouble was I had plenty of desire to embark on Dan. The man. Who I was quite sure could make me happy.

4

The green-eyed monster

During those first few weeks I threw myself into my work and enjoyed making new friends in the office. This included Dan's girlfriend, Jane, who worked in HR. She seemed an unlikely match for Dan. I got more and more jealous about them and frequently had to wrestle with the green-eyed monster, who seemed to be lurking round every corner. I would never have made a move on Dan though – however much I wanted him. And anyway, I assumed that Jane and Dan were happy together and had no idea if he even found me attractive. Hopefully it would get easier in time and I would find someone else to amuse me. Secretly though I continued to hope that Dan and Jane would split up and I could be a shoulder (or other body part) for Dan to cry on. I didn't feel good about this, but the attraction to Dan was simply out of my control.

In about the middle of June they did break up. The trouble was it wasn't Dan who wanted to cry on my shoulder. He arrived at work on the Monday morning after the split, with a radical new haircut and a silver Audi sports car, looking as though he didn't have a care in the world. Jane, on the other hand, looked lousy; as only a woman whose heart has been torn in two can. Absolutely shattered. Not sleeping, not eating, and wishing she was dead.

I found myself in a terrible situation. I had never admitted my feelings for Dan to Jane and I felt like a complete traitor as I consoled her and made all the right noises. What a cow. I could have mooed for England. Despite this I couldn't help but be pleased that Dan was now a free man. I knew in my heart that I should have been honest with Jane, but it was too late for honesty now. Besides, I still didn't think Dan had given me a second look, so I would have been hurting Jane needlessly. Oh what a tangled web. I knew that this was one episode in my life that would come back and bite me on the bum.

My discovery that Dan had indeed given me a second look, and apparently wanted to give me several more, came when we bumped into each other at head office in London soon after his split from Jane.

'Hi, Lucy! I didn't know you were up here today. I was just on my way for a coffee if you fancy one.'

As he spoke, the butterflies I always felt in his presence started their fluttering.

'Oh! Yes! Er… hello!' I stammered. I was so busy thinking just how much I would like to join him for 'one' that I couldn't get my brain and mouth to work in unison. I groaned inwardly, thinking Dan must be seeing me as completely gauche. 'Coffee, lovely. Yes, coffee would be lovely. Yes. Coffee.' Good grief Lucy Shaw, I reprimanded myself, you're like a star-struck teenager whose crush has just deigned to speak to you. Get a grip, woman! More inward groaning as I thought how much I wanted to get a grip. On Dan.

Finally, in an attempt to get a grip – on reality – I mentally kicked myself, took a deep, calming breath and turned towards the canteen. For once in my life I was very sure about what I wanted.

'If I'd known you were coming up today, we could have driven up in one car,' Dan remarked as he followed me down the corridor.

'That would have been the sensible thing to do,' I replied, trying to keep my voice steady. The thought of being alone in a confined space with this man for any length of time had sent the butterflies into hyper-drive. Just being close to Dan made me feel a little faint. That's all I need, fall over in a dead faint and knock myself out.

Thankfully, Dan seemed not to notice my ridiculous behaviour and we were soon sitting at a corner table chatting about work and getting on famously. Well, God knows Dan had the same effect on me as a well-known celeb might. It was a relief to be sitting down as it was much easier to disguise my trembling with my legs tucked under the table. My long legs were encased in the trousers of my trusty interview suit once more, which I would have been extremely grateful for had the fainting thing happened – this was neither the time nor the place for Dan to get a flash of my undies. I was pleased to have made more of an effort with my appearance than usual: this might be the best chance I ever had of making sure Dan really 'noticed' me.

I don't know if it was intentional or not, but we avoided any mention of Jane. I did, however, experience a pang of guilt when she popped, unbidden, into my head. Sorry, Jane, but I could no more resist him than not breathe.

As our untouched coffees went cold on the Formica in front of us, Dan and I were soon arranging a casual date for a walk with Jasper, of whom I now had joint custody and who was due for a weekend visit soon. Somehow, a walk with my dog didn't seem like a real 'date' and therefore less of a betrayal of Jane. But who was I kidding?

5

a date with destiny?

Saturday - it was the last Saturday of June - dawned bright and sunny: a perfect day for a non-date with a gorgeous male. And Dan wasn't half bad either. I made a conscious effort to look as though I'd made very little effort getting ready. Faded blue jeans and a peachy-coloured t-shirt, no make-up and my hair loose and natural. I didn't want to scare Dan off by appearing too desperate to impress. (Yes, OK, so I could have given a very desperate person a damn good run for his money.) I felt like a giddy schoolgirl about to meet her very first boyfriend rather than a thirty-four-year-old divorcee with joint custody of one large dog.

Jasper and I drove to the agreed meeting place, parked the car and settled down to wait for Dan. Nice one, Lucy, arriving thirty minutes early. That doesn't smack of desperation *at all*. Still, Dan wouldn't know how early I'd arrived. Unless he did the same thing of course. And then it wouldn't matter, because we'd both look as desperate as each other.

It was, however, another twenty-five minutes before Dan pulled up in his silver Audi. He parked in the space next to my little blue Fiesta and we just turned to each other and smiled. At this point the butterflies in my tummy doubled their efforts and I had to catch my breath as they threatened to flutter up my throat and out of my mouth. I thought I might actually be sick. Now that really would be attractive. I took a deep breath to calm my nerves and concentrated on getting Jasper out of the car.

Dogs, like children, are great ice-breakers. Jasper bounded up to Dan and greeted him like a long-lost friend, wagging his tail enthusiastically and slobbering ever so slightly on his hand. I admitted to myself that I'd quite like to slobber on Dan too, but settled for a smile and a hello. Inside my tail was wagging too though. I couldn't believe that this man, whom I'd admired from afar all these months, was here smiling at me and stroking my dog. Lucky dog. Said lucky dog brought me back to my senses with a tug on his lead, impatient to be off on his walk.

'Have you ever been to Heathfield Common?' I asked Dan as we headed out of the car park. 'I once came here on a geography field trip with school,' I added before Dan had a chance to answer. I carried on with my nervous prattling, 'I thought it was about halfway between your house and mine – seemed only right to share the driving.'

If I'd given the destination any real thought, I would not have picked it for a first non-date. Unfortunately, ever since we arranged to meet, my brain had been otherwise engaged. You see, Heathfield Common was a bog. A very beautiful bog, but not the easiest of places to walk with any semblance of elegance. Thankfully I had on pretty decent walking boots and managed to jump over the worst bits of bog with, if not the grace of gazelle, at least not like a stampeding hippo. Or so I hoped.

It was going really well. The sun continued to shine down on us and we just walked, enjoying each other's company and watching Jasper bounding along with his tail in the air, not a care in the world. I'd been so worried about how Jasper would cope with his 'mum and dad' splitting up, but he was a really well-adjusted dog and had adapted to his dual life brilliantly. What a relief. I could only imagine what it must be like for couples who split and have human children to share!

We were walking in single file owing to the narrowness of the path, with Dan in the lead, when suddenly I felt a sharp stinging on my breast. And another. Ouch! I could also hear a faint buzzing and I realised that some sort of biting insect was down the front of my t-shirt. Oh great, I thought. Do I draw attention to my chest this early in the relationship? (Although, let's be frank, Dan had probably copped a good look at my substantial breasts the very first time he clapped eyes on me. They were hard to miss as they arrived in a room some time before I did.)

I decided not to let on what was happening down the front of my top and tried to discreetly shake the little bugger out when Dan wasn't looking. My plan would have worked, except that when Dan turned back to me, there was a small patch of blood seeping through my t-shirt. So there I am explaining what has happened and feeling a right tit. (Actually, it was the left one, but allow me a little artistic license.) Dan was immediately concerned for me and impressed at my lack of girly hysterics.

'Oh my God, Lucy, what's happened? You're bleeding!' Dan looked and sounded genuinely worried.

'Oh, yeah, don't worry, it's nothing. Just been stung or something. Looks worse than it is,' I pooh-poohed, with a wave of my hand.

'Are you sure? Has whatever it was that bit you gone?' Was he offering to have a look for it? I wondered.

'Yep. Either that or I squished it,' I dismissed, as tempting as the idea of him having a quick fumble was.

'Thank goodness! How about we find a pub somewhere for a drink and some lunch, Lucy? I could do with a cold one.'

Shower, I thought. 'Sounds good,' I said.

Jasper's lolling tongue indicated his agreement and we set off, this time in one car. Mine actually, as I didn't want Dan's covered in hair and slobber. Not yet anyway. We found a country pub with shady tables in the garden and a bowl of cold water for hot dogs, and were soon enjoying ice-cold cokes, followed by cheeseburgers and chips. (Erk! I hoped he liked a woman with a good appetite.)

Dan was great company and I still had to pinch myself from time to time to make sure I wasn't dreaming. After lunch we wandered round a nearby vineyard. It was then that Dan took my hand for the first time. I felt as though I'd been plugged into the mains as electricity coursed through my body at his touch. The butterflies had morphed into sack racers and took off in my tummy with increased vigour making me feel faint again. The little chubsters had obviously been to McDonalds for lunch and had a darn sight more than a Happy Meal while they were there. We walked on a little further and came to the most perfect country house next to the path. It really was like something out of a fairy tale. And not a grim one either. When Dan turned me towards him and kissed me, even Snow White would have regained consciousness. I had never felt anything like it before. Fireworks were going off in my head and a troupe of acrobats had taken up residence in my stomach. For the rest of the afternoon I had a Cheshire-cat grin plastered on my face. Things could not have been more purr-fect...

Apart from the fact that Dan shared a house with my esteemed boss, Mike the prat, a skinny ginger-haired, goatee-sporting Scouser who'd also migrated south. If I'm being completely honest, I was also a little worried about the age difference as Dan was only twenty-seven. Yes, I had myself a toy boy. And I loved it. And very soon I would love him too.

I broke some golden date rules I'm afraid and stayed the night with Dan. So much for not kissing until the third date. I wondered briefly if Dan would think I was a right old slapper or if he'd still respect me in the morning. Luckily Mike was away that weekend and we had the house to ourselves. Jasper made himself right at home and I took this as a good sign. Animals have great instincts don't they? I was pretty sure I hadn't hooked up with an axe-wielding psycho.

At least Dan knew I hadn't planned to stay the night – I didn't have an overnight bag stashed in the boot of my car or a toothbrush and clean knickers in the glove-box. Proof, if it were really needed, was the absence of anything to soak my contact lenses in overnight. I didn't fancy driving home the next day without them and didn't have my glasses with me. I figured I had two options: a) sleep in them and wake up looking like I'd got really bad conjunctivitis, or b) concoct some homemade saline solution to put them in. I didn't fancy a) for fear of scaring Dan, so we mixed up some salt and boiled water, dropped the lenses in and hoped for the best.

When Dan had taken me in his arms, any worries I'd had vanished. Every one of my senses felt heightened, and my skin burned wherever his lips or hands touched me. As he trailed fire along my thighs with his fingers, his kisses were searing a path down my neck. Throwing my head back, I arched myself towards

31

Dan, unable to wait any longer to become one with him.

When I awoke the next morning to see Dan smiling down at me I knew respect was not going to be an issue. Either that or he rather liked slappers. We agreed to keep our emerging relationship under wraps to save Jane's feelings and prevent any awkwardness for me with Mike. That was going to be no mean feat in the circumstances, especially since I wanted to shout it from the rooftops. (Not literally as I hated heights, but you know what I mean.) Even the scratchy stinging discomfort of my salty contact lenses couldn't dampen my mood as I kissed Dan goodbye. As Jasper and I set off on the drive home I thought I must be the happiest woman alive. Life wasn't just good, it was bloody brilliant. This must be what I had been searching for: a man who set me alight with a passion I have never before experienced. My ex Rob was wrong after all. I knew I had found a man I could really love, and my instincts were screaming that Dan felt the same.

After I had taken Jasper back to his 'dad' that evening (with much less of a pull on my heartstrings than usual) I went home to catch up on all those boring but necessary jobs like washing and ironing clothes ready for work on Monday and dealing with the post. I spring cleaned my room too and put clean sheets on the bed. Just in case. Then it was time to catch up with my housemate Carrie as I knew she'd be eager to hear all about my non-date with Dan. As I told Carrie what had happened between Dan and me I couldn't wipe the grin off my face. Even after we'd settled down to Sunday night TV I kept catching myself smirking like some deranged loon. But I couldn't help myself. All my Christmases and birthdays had come at once. And they weren't the only things.

6

Number five is alive!

I was actually the fifth woman from work that Dan had been out with and was soon to earn the nickname 'Number Five'. (And 'Bitch'. But that was only after Jane found out.) To be honest I felt as though I could have moved mountains had the need arisen; that summer I was so happy it was positively sickening. Number Five was most definitely alive. Admittedly I felt bad about betraying Jane, but with Dan by my side I could cope with anything. Besides, I'd never been called a bitch before, so that was a bit of a novelty. (Who are you kidding, Lucy? You only just managed to hold back the tears when it happened. But, if I remember rightly, they came that night, when no one could see them.)

Of course it was neither possible nor desirable to keep our relationship secret for long. Dan soon confessed to Mike that he was seeing me. Rather that, we decided, than Mike catch me coming out of Dan's bedroom wearing only a Liverpool FC shirt and a big grin. And we wanted to tell the world we were together; we wanted to hold hands in public and not waste a moment of our time together. I knew how hurt and upset Jane would be, and I was right, but my feelings for Dan were simply irresistible. I consoled myself with the knowledge that Jane and I hadn't been especially close and that I hadn't been responsible for them splitting up. It was small consolation when she did find out and I felt terrible for causing her such pain, but Dan was *the one* and I couldn't have fought my feelings for him. Even if I had wanted to.

It was a relief to have everything out in the open. (And I mean *everything*. If this was a text message, I would add a winking smiley face. And maybe a 'LOL' and several exclamation marks.) I was so very much in love and happier than I'd ever been. I'd found the man of my dreams and was lucky enough to be the woman of his (undoubtedly rather wetter) ones. Winking smiley and LOL!!!!

Those first few weeks with Dan were some of the happiest of my life. Dan was the best thing that had ever happened to me and I knew he felt the same. We soon became inseparable. Except when Liverpool were playing of course, but he couldn't help that. Even though he had left Liverpool, he was still a fanatical supporter. After all football is almost a religion in that part of the world and heaven forbid I should come between a man and his god. His place of worship was the Kop, and Anfield was his Mecca. As a season ticket holder, he made regular pilgrimages to this holy site – most home matches in fact – and prayed for many a miracle with his fellow congregants. But I figured there were worse things than being a football widow. (Being a widow for instance.) And with Dan away, I had the perfect opportunity to spend time with my girlfriends.

I knew Dan had a bit of a reputation as a commitment-phobe, especially as he appeared to be working his way through the female members of staff, but I didn't let that bother me in those early days. I was far too busy being sickeningly happy to worry about the future. Besides, Dan was showing every sign that he was serious about our relationship and it wasn't long before he took me to meet his parents who were warm and welcoming when we arrived at their house in Birmingham, and, if they disapproved of their son dating an older woman who also happened to be a divorcee, they didn't let on.

In early August, Dan took me on a romantic sunshine holiday to Majorca and I thought my heart would burst with joy when he took me in his arms on our last night on the island. We were standing on the balcony of our room at the Hotel Son Palou, overlooking the infinity pool to the mountains beyond, and I had my head nuzzled into the warmth of his chest. I could feel the rapidness of his heart beat: it was a match for the fast fluttering of my own. I sighed with pure happiness as Dan lifted my face to his, our eyes meeting and locking.

'I love you, Lucy,' Dan whispered, his eyes never leaving mine.

'I love you too,' I whispered back, feeling faint and breathless.

It was the most perfect of moments and I didn't want it to end. Later, as we lay curled around one another after making slow, sweet love, I was truly and completely happy.

Life really didn't get any sweeter than that moment, when I realised this was the man I wanted to spend the rest of my life with. We returned from our week abroad more blissful than ever.

7

My new best friend

It was in mid-August, just after our return from holiday and a couple of months after I started seeing Dan, that I met Freya. She had come for an interview and was sitting in reception when I arrived at work one morning. Freya (I only discovered her name later) was the sort of woman other women hated on sight: tall, slim with long blonde hair and a beautiful face enhanced by well-applied make-up. She looked amazing and, as irrational as it was, I felt very threatened just by her presence in the building. She got the job (no surprise there as she had a male interviewer who was obviously impressed by her… er… credentials) and I tried to rein in the hostility which was galloping through me. I didn't want to feel that hostility at seeing such an image of female perfection, but I just couldn't stop myself. My own insecurities were screaming at me and my instincts were whispering that she was trouble.

However, after a couple of weeks of getting to know Freya (she ended up working in my department) I started to wonder if my gut instincts about her had been wrong. She seemed open and friendly and really quite good fun. We started to build a friendship which over a month or so developed into something really special.

I will admit that I was still relieved to find out she was living with her long-term boyfriend and therefore less likely to be interested in Dan. I subdued my insecurities, let down my guard and welcomed Freya into my life with open arms. We spent more and more time together and soon became the best of friends. We would go clubbing together at weekends and I remember one particular night out for which we had to dress in school uniform.

Getting ready to go out was half the fun, and that night was a riot as we squeezed ourselves into short navy skirts, white shirts with very few buttons done up, and tied in a knot at the waist. Stockings and high heeled boots replaced long navy socks and sensible shoes, and old school ties were tied loosely round our necks. We completed the look with our hair in bunches, freckles on our faces, lollipops to suck on and edible necklaces made from multi-coloured bits of candy. I wouldn't have dreamed of turning up at my old girls' school looking like it: I could just imagine the apoplectic look on the headmistress's face if I had. And our old bus driver might well have had a stroke at the wheel. You can make your own jokes out of that one.

We were usually half-cut by the time we staggered up the cellar stairs and out of the house, which was probably just as well on this occasion as our outfits took some confidence to carry off. Judging by the appreciative look on the taxi driver's face when we set off for Jumpin' Jaks, however, we were looking good.

As we queued to get into the club about ten minutes later, we couldn't help but smile at the guys wearing schoolboy shorts and caps. With hindsight, we must have all looked ridiculous, but at the time it was all just a great laugh. We were all in the same boat – think banana boat on an 18-30 holiday – and all up for a good night, without the threat of homework or detention at the end of it.

The night didn't disappoint and we attracted the attention of some very cute guys. We were sufficiently drunk not to find it a bit weird to be chatted up by a man in school uniform. I was particularly flattered when a much younger man approached me:

'God, you look amazing!' he said. 'Soooooo sexy!'

It was such a fantastic ego boost, and I sucked cheekily on my ever-shrinking lollipop before replying. 'Thanks, you don't look too bad yourself.' I was tempted to add 'for someone in kindergarten', but resisted the urge.

'So, how old are you?' I asked.

'Nineteen,' came the reply.

'Jeez, I'm almost old enough to be your mother!'

'Well, you sure as hell don't look like any mother I ever met. And you can't be a day over twenty-five.'

I could have kissed him at the point. I didn't. It would have felt inappropriate. He'd only just come out of puberty. But at that point I felt a million dollars.

'Look,' I said. 'I won't be meeting you behind the bike shed any time soon, but if you want you can nibble on my necklace.' I leaned my head back and to the side, allowing easy access to the pastel-coloured confection round my neck. It tickled as he bit off a few beads. It must have looked as though I was being attacked by a vampire, but it was all good clean fun. (Although my neck was a little sticky afterwards.)

That night was one of many great times I had with Freya and I was pleased I hadn't let my first impressions stop me from getting to know her.

Before long I couldn't imagine my life without Freya in it. We grew ever closer as the months went by and she was the only girlfriend I had ever shared a bed with. I'd never been comfortable sharing a bed with anyone other than a male partner (human or dog) but I made an exception for Freya because she was so matter of fact about it. I guess that was the ultimate act of trust for me. There's something very intimate about sleeping with someone. And I mean sleeping. When you're asleep you're more vulnerable somehow. Will I talk in my sleep? Will I dribble on the pillow? Or worse, will I roll over and cuddle the person next to me? But I put aside my fears for this woman who had become so important a part of my life. I don't really know why it was different with Freya. It certainly wasn't because I had any feelings for her other than those of a deep friendship, which we both made very clear the first time we shared a bed:

'Don't be trying any funny business, Missy,' I joked to Freya as I pulled on my pyjamas. I normally slept naked, but I wasn't *that* relaxed about the whole sharing thing.

'Er... don't flatter yourself, Luce! Even if I was that way inclined, you so wouldn't be my type!'

'Charming! And why might that be?' I threw back, pretending to be offended.

'Gentlewomen prefer blondes!' Freya laughed as she hopped into her side of the bed.

'Oh, really? Is there something you haven't told me, young lady?'

'That's for me to know!' Freya said with a smile, flicking her long golden hair back over her shoulder.

I laughed, fairly sure she was only winding me up.

We became each other's confidantes and we shared our hopes and fears with the openness only two close female friends can achieve.

8

Let the bells ring out for Christmas!

Even as summer turned to autumn, the heat didn't go out of my relationship with Dan. I celebrated my thirty-fifth birthday, at the end of October, in the arms of the man I had waited so long to find. And the wait had been worth every second. And, not only had I found the man of my dreams, I also had a new best friend, in Freya. I was a lucky girl.

The cherry on the rich, gooey icing of the perfectly risen cake that was my life came when I unwrapped my Christmas presents from Dan. He'd left me with an armful of parcels before heading up to his parents for the holiday, and I was struggling like a small child not to let my excitement get the better of me and rip them open before Christmas Day. I made it to December the twenty-third.

Freya was round for the evening and proved to be as eager to find out what was inside the surprisingly well-wrapped boxes as I was.

'I really ought to wait until Christmas Day. I'm not a kid,' I said, even though I felt like one.

'No-one will know except us, and I won't tell anyone. Go on, Luce. You know you want to!' Freya was not helping.

'Oh, sod it!' I didn't need much encouragement, and was soon opening the first gift, which turned out to be a rather gorgeous teddy bear, complete with tartan dressing gown. He would definitely be taking pride of place on my bed. I was soon surrounded by a rather wonderful selection of smellies, candles, CDs and a cashmere scarf.

I'd saved the smallest box until last. It was the sort of size you might expect to contain jewellery, and I thought it might be a pair of earrings. I unwrapped it slowly; it was indeed from a jeweller's. Freya was craning her neck, trying to peep inside the box as I opened it.

'Oh my God! It's a ring! He's bought me a ring!' I genuinely hadn't been expecting it, and looked at Freya in disbelief.

'Wowzers! Didn't see that coming. Give us a look.' Freya seemed as surprised as I felt.

It wasn't a diamond engagement ring, but a Russian wedding ring: three intertwined bands of yellow, white and rose gold. Still, I knew the implication was huge and meant that Dan was committed to me. I had cured him of his commitment phobia and he wanted to be with me forever.

And that was the beginning of the end. I had successfully tamed and harnessed my wild stallion. I'd got a saddle on him (not literally obviously) and ridden him (Yeeha!) in. I had succeeded in breaking him in where so many others had tried and failed before me. I had made this elusive man mine, the man of my dreams had become my reality. This was for the rest of my life.

Unfortunately, that was when the panic set in and, inconsistent Lucy that I was, I was forced to admit that after six months I didn't want to commit to Dan, or any other man either. What the heck was wrong with me? Every time things in my life seemed to be perfect, I pressed some kind of self-destruct button. I tried to analyse why I did this, and my head was spinning with half-baked psycho-babble ideas. Did I think I didn't deserve happiness? Or was I scared that it was too good to be true, and I should therefore end it before the rot set in? I didn't know the answer. I just felt desperately sad. It looked as though Rob had been right and I was cursed to tread the same broken path as my parents.

9

The bleak mid-winter

Soon after Christmas, in the dead of winter, I had come to the conclusion that I was destined never to be really happy. I was one of those people who always wanted what they hadn't got, and once I'd got it I no longer wanted it. This was true of both men and inanimate objects. (Although the two could at times be confused.) I could see a dress in a shop window which I absolutely loved and simply had to have. I would be so sure that it would give me so much happiness once it was mine, and hanging in my wardrobe. So I would purchase the object of my desire and take it home where I would love and cherish it for years to come. Except that once I had made it mine it lost its appeal almost immediately.

The same was true with men. I fell in love at the drop of a hat and always believed that he was 'the one'. But he never was. Once I had succeeded in making that gem of a man mine his lustre started to fade and I no longer felt any attraction to this person I was so besotted with. One minute I was writing 'I love you' in socks on his bedroom floor and the next I was ready to throttle him with a pair. This was not a recipe for a happy life, just a feeling of permanent discontent and unfulfillment, made worse by my complete inability to ever really let go of the past. I may not have wanted a man anymore, but that didn't mean I wanted him to stop wanting me. I could really have done with a man-rack in my wardrobe, right next to the one for my shoes.

And so it was with Dan. We had drifted in to spring with the snow but my feelings had turned to grey slush by the time the snowdrops appeared. Dan of course noticed the change in me and he looked sad a lot of the time. I felt miserable knowing that I was the cause of his sadness. I can remember one evening him saying to me: 'The only time I make you smile now is when I do my Mick Jagger impersonation.' The confusing thing was that, although I was no longer happy with Dan, I still felt as though I was in love with him. I wasn't happy in the relationship at that time, but I still believed that one day we'd be together forever. This was a new experience for me. Although I'd always been useless at letting go of the past, I'd never regretted ending a relationship. Yes, I always regretted hurting the other person, but I always knew I was doing the right thing for me. Not this time. Even though Dan no longer made me happy, I still longed for him. What I wanted more than anything was to feel about him as I had on that first non-date, when he'd taken me in his arms and kissed me. Boy was I messed up. And about to get a whole lot more so.

It was Freya I turned to when Dan and I split up that spring. She more than anyone knew how confused I was about my feelings for this man. She was my rock, my shoulder to cry on. And I was hers soon afterwards when her own long-term relationship ended. For a while Freya practically lived with me at Carrie's and we were closer as friends than ever. I don't know what I would have done without her and I think she felt the same. Actually, make that *thought* she felt the same.

10

Tara doesn't bounce

That spring, after my split from Dan, I figured life might be easier if I didn't see him at the office every day, and I decided to look for a new job. It just so happened that my boss, Mike, was working out his notice and, when he heard of my decision, he told me there was a job for me at his new place if I wanted it. Much as I disliked working for Mike, it was still a solution and still in Maidstone thankfully. My last day was incredibly sad – I was leaving some good friends behind. But I knew that the ones who really mattered would keep in touch. And I wasn't burning all my bridges to Dan as we would be linked by our shared friends and social scene. I still lived in hope and continued to confide my feelings to Freya, who listened and hugged me and passed me tissues when I cried. We talked about some of the many good times we'd had and we laughed and cried together. Freya had become like a sister to me and I was so glad I had her in my life.

To celebrate/commiserate my last day at work, Freya and I went clubbing with a couple more of our close friends from the office: Tara and Jess. It was to prove an especially memorable night for one reason and another.

'So, back to mine after work then? I'll do us some dinner.'

'Let me guess, Luce… jacket potatoes?' Jess joked.

Tara and Freya both laughed; cooking was really not my thing.
I gave a shrug. 'You do get a choice of fillings.'

'Tuna or cheese!' the three of them chorused. I hadn't realised
quite how predictable I was.

'You could always have tuna AND cheese. Or I could really
push the boat out and open a tin of beans,' I countered.

Jess, ever the joker, put the back of her hand to her forehead
and feigned fainting in shock. We all laughed.

I knew they were only winding me up – the food was simply
to line our stomachs for the influx of alcohol which was to
follow. Smirnoff Ice was the drink du jour and we all clinked
bottles before disappearing off to bathroom or bedroom to
start getting ready.

'Put some music on, Jess,' I shouted from the bedroom, and
soon the sound of Spiller's *Groove Jet* filtered through the house.
It was shaping up to be a very good night.

After an hour or so, we all reconvened in the lounge.

'Finally!' said Jess in mock exasperation. 'Tara and I were
ready blinking ages ago. What on earth do you two get up to
that takes so long?'

'Hey! It takes time to look this good!' Freya retorted. And
look good she did. Stunning in fact.

Although the four of us were great friends, we were quite
different in many ways. Jess and Tara didn't really care if men
gave them a second look or not, while Freya and I needed the
reassurance of knowing men found us attractive. I guess Jess
and Tara were happier in their own skins and didn't depend on
the approval of others to feel confident. It was a sad admission
that Freya and I depended so much on being attractive to the
opposite sex for our sense of self-worth.

'Photos!' I shouted, waving my iPhone in the air.

It had become a tradition to take *Charlie's Angels* style pics when we were all dressed up for a night out. Looking back, it sounds so naff, but it had become part of our ritual, and it mattered.

'Gorgeous girls!' Jess remarked as she took a turn at being photographer. We did make quite a striking group: Freya and Tara, slim and beautiful blondes, Jess and I contrasting brunettes. (Who hadn't exactly fallen out of the ugly tree.) Tara was especially slim and had the looks of a Nordic beauty. One of those blondes who tans perfectly and evenly and always seems to glow with health. She was also the most settled – and sensible – of the four of us and lived with her fiancé, Nick. Tara rarely drank and we all felt responsible for keeping an eye on her when she did. Even with her toned, tanned and tiny tummy lined with one of my infamous jacket potatoes, Tara would reach her alcohol limit early.

Jess, on the other hand, despite her slim frame, could drink most men under the table. Even at the end of a night out she still seemed as sober as a judge. She was also the youngest of the group at just nineteen and still lived with her parents, but Jess had a wise head on her shoulders and an old soul. She would be the one to keep us out of trouble and had taken it upon herself to keep an especially close eye on Tara. This was fine by me and Freya as it meant we could keep a close eye on the talent. We were both single now and looking for an ego boost to prove we still had what it takes. We were definitely on a bit of a mission that night.

'God, I'm soooo going to miss seeing you guys at work every day!' I was already a little bit tipsy and in danger of getting

48

overly sentimental.

Seeing that I was on the verge of tears, Freya came over and gave me a big hug.

'We'll miss you too, silly! But we'll all keep in touch and see you loads. You don't get rid of us that easily.'

'I don't want to get rid of you – I don't want to break up our gang.' In truth, I hated the fact that the three of them would still be working together. I was worried about becoming an 'outsider' – no longer part of the inner sanctum. I was jealous I suppose. And mixed up. As usual. Didn't want to stay in the job, but didn't want to leave either. Classic Lucy conundrum.

'Cheer up, you miserable cow!' Jess said with a light punch to the top of my arm. 'We're meant to be having fun! More vodka!'

'Sorry! Take no notice. I'm being pathetic. Let's get this show on the road; taxi's due any minute.'

'Just time for one more ickle dwinkie then,' slurred Tara.

'Ickle dwinkie, Tara? Really?! You need to slow down!' I joked.

She did sound a little worse for wear and we should have heeded this warning, but we were all too hyped up about the night ahead to really register it, and, at that same moment, the taxi driver beeped his horn and all thoughts of Tara's level of intoxication were forgotten. The taxi driver grinned when we all trooped out the front door a few moments later and climbed into his cab. Jess, being the responsible adult, rode up front.

'To Images Nightclub, my good man!' she instructed.

Giggles from the back seat. Thankfully the driver had a sense of humour.

By happy coincidence, when we arrived at the club we discovered it was ladies' night and the Chippendales were performing.

None of us had ever seen strippers before (what sheltered lives we'd led) and thought it would be a giggle if nothing else. We were quite sure we wouldn't be screaming and throwing our knickers but we had open minds about the whole thing.

So there we were, front row, a few vodkas worse for wear, screaming along with the best of them as five perfect male specimens strutted their stuff. I have to admit to panicking when one of them came up to me expecting a hand with his zip. I backed off and let Freya do the honours. I guess I'm just an old-fashioned girl deep down. Once their pants had come off and they'd started to swing their bits around as though they were going to lasso something, I rather lost interest. I did think some things should be left to the imagination and men looked better with their undies on. Still, it made a change and made the evening all the more memorable. Not that we needed to worry about ever forgetting that night. Tara took care of that…

'Ladies,' announced Jess. 'I'm afraid I have to love you and leave you.'

It was almost midnight and Jess's dad was picking her up as there was no public transport to her village after about eight p.m. It really was the back of beyond.

'Make sure you look after Tara.' This to me and Freya.

'Yes, Mum!'

'Freya, I'm serious! She's looking a bit unsteady.'

Unlike Jess, who still seemed to be completely sober despite matching a now decidedly tiddly me and Freya drink for drink. So, Freya and I made our drunken assurances and Jess left, with a worried backward glance. I don't think she had a great deal of faith in us, but we felt invincible. The vodka effect.

'Let's check out the bar upstairs,' suggested Freya when Jess was out of sight.

'Sounds like a plan. Come on, Tara.' I was happy to take Freya's lead and follow her up the spiral iron staircase, concentrating hard as I made my drunken ascent to the as yet unexplored upper level.

Had I not been as drunk, I would have made sure Tara went in front of me. It had taken all my focus and concentration to make it up the dark, winding and rather crowded staircase. I don't know why, but about halfway up, I turned to check on Tara's progress. Maybe it was a sixth sense. 'You OK, T?' I said as I turned. But Tara wasn't behind me. 'Tara? Freya! I can't see Tara; I'm going back down to look for her.' As I spoke, I was already tottering gingerly back down, my heart thudding in my chest. My worst fears were confirmed when I found Tara in a heap at the bottom, her head wedged between two of the metal posts.

'Oh Jesus! Tara! Are you OK? Tara! Omigod omigod omigod!' I suddenly felt very sober. And very scared. I should have been looking after her.

'Out of the way, please,' a burly security guard had appeared out of the darkness, scooped Tara up as if she weighed nothing, and carried her to the first aid room.

By now Freya had caught up with us and looked as pale and shocked as I felt. 'Jesus, Luce, is she OK?'

'I don't know! I don't know. We should have been watching her, Frey!' I was on the verge of tears, but knew I had to keep it together for Tara's sake.

'Only one of you can come in with her,' the bouncer said as he laid Tara on a couch like the ones in doctors' surgeries.

I went in with Tara and I sat on the bed holding her while she was sick. Really, really sick. All over me. It was a very sobering experience. Her head was bleeding badly and another member of staff was applying pressure to the cuts. It wasn't long before we heard that an ambulance had arrived to take Tara to the hospital. I found Freya outside the room sobbing. She'd had an encounter with the Chippendales as they left the building: 'They tried to hit on me,' she wailed. I think she was really pissed off at the timing.

I rode in the back of the ambulance with Tara, while Freya rode up front.

'I don't want to die, Lucy,' Tara sobbed. She really was very drunk.

'You're not going to die, Tara. I promise,' taking her hand and holding her long hair back as she continued to be sick.

Feeling lousy, and horribly guilt-ridden, we had phoned Tara's fiancé from the hospital and stayed with her while they stitched the cuts on her head. Freya and I actually looked worse than Tara by then. I think the shock had set in. Once Tara was safely on her way home with worried fiancé Nick it was 3:30 a.m. and it suddenly dawned on us that Nick had been our lift home too. Oops. We hadn't budgeted for a taxi and were stranded in A&E. The only person we could think of to phone for a lift was Dan. Great.

The next morning saw me and Freya staggering blearily round town in search of a card and some flowers for Tara. We looked and felt like death after the intense experience of the previous night, and very little sleep. McDonalds for breakfast hadn't dealt with our hangovers, but we felt so guilty about what had happened to Tara that we were determined to go and see that she was OK. It was with some trepidation that we knocked on Tara's front door an hour or so later. And bugger me if she wasn't sitting up in bed looking as right as rain. It really was the ultimate drunken night out. Not one I would like to repeat, but an experience none the less.

11

The love letter

Soon after this episode, in early April, Tara and Jess both left their jobs and Freya alone remained working with Dan. We all still socialised together from time to time. While I enjoyed everyone's company, I think deep down I was lonely. Part of me still believed that Dan and I would get back together one day. Freya and I were as close as ever, but then she started to mention Dan more and more. They had been thrown together when Tara and Jess left and were apparently spending a lot of time together. I asked Freya about their growing closeness.

'Sounds as though you and Dan are seeing a lot of each other. Something I should know about?' I asked, trying to sound jokey.

'Don't be daft! We're just friends. We both miss you, Tara and Jess being around, I s'pose. We're united in our grief!'

'Take no notice. I'm just being a wally. I still miss him though, Frey. It's hard.'

'If it really bothers you, I'll back off and not see him as much.'

I wasn't completely reassured when Freya said they were just friends, but she knew how much I still cared about him and how great was the hurt when I heard they were hanging out together. I tried to reassure myself that Freya wouldn't cross the line, wouldn't break the unwritten rule, between friends. I felt a bit hypocritical when I thought of how I'd hurt Jane by dating

Dan, but my casual friendship with her couldn't compare with the bond I had with Freya.

The belief that Dan was still my future was shattered one morning when I found a hand-delivered letter from Freya on the doormat at Carrie's, telling me that she and Dan were now together and in love and they were both really sorry. Not half as sorry as I was. I fell apart then. My best friend was in bed with the love of my life, and my housemate was in bed upstairs with another ex. (Don't ask! Maybe I'll tell you later!) *What the hell was going on here*, I wondered? *Was this my new role in life? Train 'em up and move 'em on? I should start charging for the service.* For someone like me, who didn't ever really let go of anyone, this was just too much. The two people I would normally have turned to were suddenly unapproachable and I had no-one to pour my heart out to. Boy did I feel sorry for myself. I guess I knew how Jane had felt now. Did it serve me right? Was Jane right when she called me 'Bitch'? My actions had indeed come back to bite me hard on the bum and Freya had turned out to be the goddess of divine retribution. Although I use the word goddess reluctantly, for reasons which will become clear.

I could just about cope with the loss of Dan, but losing my best friend at the same time was almost more than I could bear. Freya had been everything to me and, without her, I felt so very lost and desperately alone. Depression had become my new worst friend. I started to struggle to hold it together at work too. My boss, and Dan's housemate, Mike, called me into his office one morning:

'Shut the door, Lucy,' he said.

That was never a good sign, I thought as I closed the door and sat down in the chair next to Mike's desk. I could feel the eyes of my colleagues on me, feeling sorry for me I suppose. I wished the office blinds were closed.

'Right. Lucy. I know the news about Dan and Freya has hit you hard, but you can't let it affect your performance at work.'

I just gulped back the lump that was permanently in my throat these days, nodded and looked at the floor.

'You have to be professional, Lucy. You have to leave your personal problems at the door when you come in to work each day. We all have to. Do you understand?'

Another gulp. A nod. Holding back the tears.

Of course, rationally, I understood what Mike was saying, but it didn't make any difference. I didn't seem to be able to control my emotions or the way I was feeling. I had fallen into a big black hole and could see no way of climbing out of it. My emotions felt like hands around my throat and threatened to choke me, making it hard to breathe evenly. I felt at the moment, that if I let the tears come, they would never, ever, stop.

'So, take a coffee break and come back in ten minutes with that happy face we all know and love, eh, Lucy?'

'OK,' I managed to squeak, and somehow got out of Mike's office and to the loo without the cracks in my emotional dam bursting. It felt as though I was a stone chip in a windscreen and every second, the frost was penetrating more. I knew it was only a matter of time before the chip became a crack and the crack shattered.

Shutting myself in a cubicle, I sat down on the loo seat and tried to breathe. How on earth was I going to be back at my desk in ten minutes, looking like I didn't have a care in the world, when that whole world was in tatters?

I knew I didn't have long before someone came looking for me and I realised I couldn't hide in the ladies for the rest of the day, but I really didn't think I could hold my emotions together back at my desk, with all eyes on me. If anyone was kind or sympathetic to me, I'd fall apart. Then, just as the automatic air freshener went off, engulfing me in a cloud of citrus, I had a bit of a brainwave as I remembered a job I'd been putting off because it involved spending several hours alone with boxes and boxes of files in the dusty old archives. Boxes would be perfect company in my current mood.

I gave my face a splash with cold water, smoothed down my hair, straightened my skirt and, with a deep breath, I walked back down the corridor to accounts. *You can do this, Lucy Shaw, you've been doing it your whole life,* I was telling myself. *Hold your head up high, plaster a smile on your face and act your butt off!*

And that's what I did. The act held long enough for me to explain my plan for the rest of the day to my colleagues (who looked relieved, to be honest), grab the few things I'd need, and disappear to the cardboard catacombs. I knew I was only putting off facing up to things, but all I could do was get through that one day without falling apart.

12

Carrie me home

Eventually, that longest of days came to an end, and, at five p.m., I switched off the lights, sending my cardboard colleagues into darkness, and closed the door to the archives with a sigh. I knew that I had to talk to someone about how I was feeling, otherwise I simply wouldn't be able to get through another day without losing the plot. I said the briefest of good-nights to the guys in the office and half ran to the car park, breathing a sigh of relief when I had closed the car door and was safely alone again. I clicked the lock down on the door – I'm not sure why – started the engine and drove quickly out of the staff car park and headed for home.

Arriving home about ten minutes later, I let myself into the house and shut the front door behind me, leaning back against it as if my legs would no longer support me. I just wanted to slide to the floor and stay there, but I forced myself to travel those few more steps to the sofa, grateful that the front door opened straight into the lounge. I really didn't think my legs could have carried me any further. Dropping my jacket and bag on to the teal-coloured cushion beside me, I sank on to the sofa, the cushions exhaling in sympathy.

'Lucy, are you OK? Are you ill? Why are you sitting in the dark?'

Carrie's words brought me out of a sort of trance. I had no

idea how much time had passed, but the room had grown dark around me. I hadn't moved an inch from my place on the sofa, unaware of the passing of time, or the darkening of the room.

'Carrie. Hi. What time is it?'

'It's eight thirty! I went for a drink with some girls from the office after work. What's wrong, Lucy? Has something happened?'

'Um. Yeah… I guess,' I replied. 'I wanted to talk to you, to tell you, but…' I didn't know how to go on.

'But I was too wrapped up in myself, wasn't I?' Carrie said.

'Oh, no, please don't feel that, Carrie! You have every right to be enjoying every second of your new relationship. I just didn't want to… intrude, I guess. It's been kind of awkward.'

'I'm sorry, Lucy. I should still have realised that something was wrong. Let me make us a cuppa, and you can tell me what's happened.'

A few minutes later, Carrie had made tea, clicked the heating on to take the chill off the room, closed the curtains and put the lamp on in the corner of the lounge, turning off the harsh, main light.

'Right, talk to me, Lucy,' she said.

And I did. And once I started, I didn't, couldn't, stop until I had poured every bit of hurt and confusion I was feeling. The dam had indeed burst; the windscreen shattered.

Carrie just held my hand and listened. And passed me tissues as I sobbed the words out. When the words finally dried up and all that was left was the hiccoughing residue of my sobs, Carrie simply put her arms around me and said, 'I'm so very sorry, Lucy,' and held me tightly in her strong little arms, as if she would never let me go.

That's when I realised I wasn't alone. I didn't have to go through this on my own. I still had Carrie.

My head was splitting from the crying, but I felt an enormous sense of relief at having opened the floodgates and unburdening myself.

'I wish you'd told me sooner, Lucy. I could've helped. I'm sorry you felt you couldn't come to me.'

'I'm sorry too. I didn't want to spoil things for you – you've been so happy lately. I didn't want to bring you down.'

'I'm your friend, silly – in good times AND bad. You can always come to me – it doesn't matter what's going on in my life, I'm here for you. Just like you're there for me.'

'Thank you. I do feel a lot better now. I'm such a wally, aren't I?'

'No, you just don't like asking for help because you don't want to be a nuisance. But you're not a nuisance, you spoon!'

'Well, I feel like crap, but I also feel like I can cope now, thanks to you. Thank you, Carrie. I really don't know what I'd do without you.'

'You're stronger than you realise, Lucy. Look at how far you've come since your marriage ended. We're survivors, you and me. Now, why don't you go and have a soak in the bath while I rustle up some supper for us both.'

Thirty or so minutes later, warm and pink from the bath, I managed to eat some tomato soup and a roll, without the lump in my throat getting in the way for the first time in days. And then, after giving Carrie one last thankyou hug, I took myself of to bed and fell almost immediately into a deep, dreamless, sleep.

13

The fairy tale just got grim

Despite hurting me to be with Dan, Freya couldn't even be faithful to him. Rumours about her inability to be faithful to Dan abounded and it hurt that she had destroyed our friendship for a relationship which she obviously wasn't that serious about. I wondered if she just wanted Dan because he'd been mine. I guess my first impressions of Freya had been right after all. I thought about telling Dan, but that just wasn't my style. Besides, it would probably have seemed like sour grapes coming from me. I just had to try and rebuild my shattered life.

The building work suffered another setback when I found out that Freya and Dan had got engaged, and were planning a grand wedding in a Scottish castle. In light of the rumours, I couldn't understand why she was marrying him. Maybe she didn't know how to get out of it and didn't want to hurt Dan? Maybe, looking back to my marriage to Rob, we were more similar than I cared to admit. Anyway, any lingering hopes I had of getting back together with Dan died that day. I thought about Dan and Freya every day for a very long time. Eventually I could sometimes go a whole day without thinking about them, but not often. I just waited for time to do its stuff and tried to summon up some enthusiasm for my own restoration work.

14

Maybe baby

Well, single, and living in a house-share was not where I thought I'd be at the grand old age of thirty-five. Much as I loved Carrie and enjoyed sharing a house with her, somewhere down the line, things had gone horribly wrong and it was time to try and get my life back on track.

During the summer months, and into September, I gradually convinced myself that what was really missing from my life was not a man, but a baby. I know, you can't have one without the other, but that was a minor technicality at the time. I was at a crossroads in my life and, the more I thought about it, the more I believed that the right track led to a baby. A baby would bring me that fulfilment I longed for, wouldn't it?

I knew that I had been continually putting my biological alarm clock on snooze for years now, but hadn't turned it off. I realised that the time had come to take men a bit more seriously and to view them as potential sperm donors… I mean life partners - rather than ridiculing them and winding them up. Damn I knew I'd miss the ridiculing, but sacrifices must be made when a woman's eggs were threatening to jump out of the pan. The next willing victim – I mean man – who asked 'how do you like your eggs in the morning?' was going to wish he'd bought cereal.

But what kind of man would fit the bill? Now as a rule, I

knew that I didn't do short, bald men who smoked and had baggage. None of my family had ever smoked and I didn't like all aspects of this filthy habit. Lots of other unpleasant habits were acceptable, but not smoking. I preferred men to be taller than me so I could wear heels without towering over them. Hugs were better if the man was taller too. As for bald... well I guess that was the one thing I could compromise on. I'd always found follically challenged men attractive for some reason. Aren't they supposed to be more virile too? Definitely desirable for potential baby-making. On the subject of baggage I was, however, immoveable. Coming from a family whose genealogical tree had several grafts and umpteen suckers, I was in no hurry to further complicate matters. And I certainly didn't want to take on the role of stepmother. Wicked or otherwise. I'd had my own experiences of stepmothers and God knows I didn't ever want to inspire that sort of voodoo-doll stabbing loathing.

15

The gene Paul

So it was, safely armed with my mental list of 'don't dos', that I went to work the following day. It was a bright morning in late September, one of those autumn days that harked back to summer – an unexpected sunshine bonus that made you feel good to be alive.

And there he was. In the tea room. Decidedly short, almost completely bald, fluorescent light bouncing off his head, a packet of Marlboro Lights in his shirt pocket and a tan line on his wedding finger. Paul. I thought I remembered hearing that he was married with two little boys. So, why wasn't he wearing his wedding ring? Of course I'd seen him around the building and said hello on occasion, but I'd never really spoken to him.

'Morning,' I said.

'Good morning. Lucy, isn't it?'

'Yes, and you're Paul? You work in IT, don't you?'

'Yep. For my sins. In fact, I manage the department. Aren't you down to audit us soon?'

'Oh… er… yes that's right I am.' Auditing was my least favourite thing in the world at the best of times. I dreaded to think what a pig's ear I might make of it when the time came.

By being short and bald, he already broke two of my requirements, and if he was still married, that would break a third. Despite this, I was surprised how attracted I was to him. I couldn't help wondering if the attraction was a result of my clamouring ovaries.

We were on our own in the tea room, which was just as well because Paul suddenly blurted out that his wife had just left him.

'She walked out three weeks ago. Left me. Just like that. No *I'm sorry* or *Let's try and work it out for the boys' sakes*. She just went, without so much as a backward glance.'

'I'm so sorry. How are you coping?' I said, feeling a little bit uncomfortable at the revelation and at how inadequate my words sounded.

'It's been pretty rough, but I'm OK I guess.'

'I can only imagine how hard it's been for you.' I thought briefly about how much harder my own separation from Rob would have been had we had children, or if I would have left at all.

'I really thought I couldn't survive it at first. It's not quite as raw as it was, but it still really hurts.'

'Well, hang in there, and if you need someone to talk to, you know where to find me.' It felt like the right thing to say.

'Thanks, Lucy. That's sweet of you. I might just take you up on it sometime.'

And he did. The very next day, he came and found me at my desk and invited me over to his house.

I was up to my eyes in spreadsheets and starting to see double. As I sat up straight, stretched and turned my neck from side to side in an attempt to release some of the tension that had built up, I spotted Paul coming through the double doors to the department. It flashed into my mind that he might be coming to see me and, sure enough, he was making his way over to my desk. I immediately felt self-conscious and wondered how much of a state I looked; when concentrating on spreadsheets, I often raked my fingers through my hair in frustration and was now convinced that I looked like a scare-crow. *Hair styled by hedge. Sideways.* I groaned inwardly as I made some attempt to smooth down my hair. I hoped no-one around me had noticed my flustered state.

'Lucy, hi, you reported a problem with your PC? I was headed this way, so I thought I'd come and see if I could sort it myself. It does me good to keep my hand in.'

It took me a second to catch on, as I hadn't reported any such problem with my computer.

'Oh, yes. That's good of you. I'm sure it's a quick fix,' I mumbled.

'Let's have a look then, shall we?' Paul said as he leant in over my keyboard and starting pressing various keys which brought up menus I had never seen before. There was a definite crackle in the air between us, and I don't think it had anything to do with electronics. Again I wondered at the attraction, as Paul simply wasn't my type, but the feel of his breath on my neck as he leant over me, was undoubtedly sending pleasurable shivers down my spine.

I just sat there like a dummy while Paul 'fixed' the 'problem', not knowing what to say. I think I said 'Can you fix it?' at one point. *Smooth, Lucy*, I thought. *He's not Bob-the-Builder*.

After what seemed an eternity, but was probably only a couple of minutes, most of which time I think I was holding my breath, Paul said:

'All done. You shouldn't get that error message again.'

'Oh. Great. Thank you. That's brilliant.'

'No worries. Catch you later,' Paul replied as he turned to leave.

I was just wondering what on earth that had all been about, when I spotted a folded piece of paper with my name on it, on the desk in front of me. Glancing around to see if anyone had noticed, I opened the paper and read:

A drink at my house, 8pm tomorrow x

There followed an address and a mobile phone number. Nothing else. I was a little bit taken aback. It wasn't so much an invitation as an instruction. Feeling a little bemused, I decided to give Paul the benefit of the doubt, concluding that he was just incredibly sure of himself and the attraction between us. As it happened, I had no plans for the following night, and was intrigued enough to go.

I arrived at Paul's at 8 p.m. the following evening, and was feeling a little nervous as I pulled on to the drive of a substantial-looking detached house. Taking a deep breath, I rang the doorbell. It felt like ages before the door opened, but it can't have been more than a few seconds.

'Lucy, hi, lovely to see you. Come on in.' Paul looked happy to see me and not in the least bit nervous. Why was I always so anxious about everything in life? So uncertain. Maybe I'd be better off if my name was Lucy Unsure, the thought coming unbidden into my mind, as my thoughts so often do.

Paul led me into a cosy lounge and indicated that I should take a seat; there was a choice of armchair or sofa. Sinking into the armchair – it was an automatic choice as sitting alone suited my insecurity – I responded to Paul's offer of a drink.

'Coffee would be lovely. I won't have a glass of wine as I'm not a big wine drinker, and I'm driving, but don't let me stop you.' To be honest, I could have done with some Dutch courage right about now! (Did you know that Dutch courage refers specifically to gin? I've never drunk gin. Another random, unbidden thought from my Jack-in-a-box brain. It does make it difficult to concentrate on what someone is saying to you when this happens.)

'Er… sorry… what were you saying?' He must have thought I was totally scatty or terribly rude.

'I was just asking how you take your coffee.'

'Oh! White and one please.'

Paul was soon handing me my coffee, in a Power Rangers mug, and had a glass of red wine for himself. Cuddling the mug gave my nervous hands something to do and I felt myself starting to relax. Paul had a very calm aura somehow. I had my aura photographed once. I forced the random thought out of my mind, and my attention back to the present.

We were soon chatting comfortably about work and sharing funny anecdotes about our colleagues. As we relaxed into each other's company, the conversation soon switched to more personal matters, and Paul started to tell me about the very recent split from his wife. I could still see the pain etched around his eyes.

As Paul talked, I found myself even more attracted to him. He seemed kind and funny, and was really easy to be with. I wanted to go over and sit next to him. I wanted to kiss him. But I didn't. Two hours flew by as we chatted and got to know each other. As I was leaving, just after 10 p.m., Paul invited me over the following Saturday evening.

'We could get a Chinese or something,' he suggested.

'I'd like that,' I found myself agreeing.

As I drove home, I wondered what lay ahead. Could Paul possibly be the key to unlocking lasting happiness? Only time would tell, Lucy, I told myself, but I still worried that I wouldn't ever know for sure.

16

a small bombshell

So, there I was, the following Saturday evening, ringing Paul's doorbell again, a bottle of red wine in hand. Paul looked delighted to see me and I must admit that I wasn't quite as nervous as last time, which boded well. Leading the way into the lounge once more, Paul obscured my view temporarily.

A second or two later, though, I spied a small boy, dressed in Power Ranger pyjamas (that explained the mug, I thought), sitting on the carpet surrounded by Lego bricks. Concealing my surprise, I said hello as a small round, freckly face with a mop of strawberry blonde hair looked up at me.

'Lucy, meet Jamie, my son. Jamie, this is Lucy, the friend I told you about.'

'Hello, Lucy,' said the cutie on the carpet matter-of-factly. 'I'm building a space ship.'

'And a very impressive space ship it is, Jamie,' I replied, thinking I might be needing it to make a quick getaway. I wasn't expecting to meet Paul's kids at this early stage and had most definitely been caught off guard. Did Jamie live with him? This was stepmother territory and somewhere I'd always sworn never to set foot.

My face must have given away my slight panic, as Paul ushered me out of the room, muttering something about 'showing me round'. As Paul led the way around a rather lovely home, I spotted several baby and toddler photographs on the walls – two cute little boys, one very fair and one strawberry blonde which I assumed was Jamie, who was clearly the older of the brothers.

When we reached the kitchen, Paul turned to me:

'Sorry to spring Jamie on you, Lucy. I didn't know how to tell you about him, and I didn't want to scare you off by telling you he lives with me.' Paul sounded nervous and apologetic at the same time. 'He refused to go with his mum when she moved out with his little brother Scott.'

'Er… that's OK. He seems like a sweetie.' Well, what else could I have said? I'm not one to cause a scene. I don't do confrontation at the best (or should that be worst?) of times. Besides, it was only our second date – it's not like we were in a serious relationship.

Returning to the lounge with drinks and a Chinese takeaway menu, I sat on the carpet opposite Jamie and proceeded to start construction on a docking station for his space ship. Jamie accepted my presence unquestioningly, and I soon forgot about my initial shock at seeing him, and relaxed into what became a lovely evening, culminating in an equally lovely goodnight kiss.

OK, so Paul was a short, bald smoker with a bit of excess luggage, (think August at Heathrow), but, as baggage goes, Jamie was really rather lovely.

Things moved fast between Paul and me, although we tried to keep our rapidly blossoming relationship a secret at work as he'd only just split from his wife. (I see a pattern, here, Lucy. You and Dan kept things secret too. Doesn't this tell you that maybe something's not right? This from the angel on my right

71

shoulder. Funny thing, I've always been a bit deaf in that ear.)

To be honest, we did a pretty rubbish job of hiding our feelings. We kept sneaking off to the back staircase leading to the fire exit for stolen kisses, and my computer developed an awful lot of problems which only the head of IT could resolve.

'Do you think your computer needs replacing, Lucy?' John, one of my colleagues, remarked after yet another visit from Paul. 'It does seem to be going wrong an awful lot.'

'Mmm… maybe,' I replied, dreamily, only half listening to what John was saying to me.

'They must be pretty serious issues for Paul to come himself, rather than sending one of his techie minions.'

'Mmm… minions… ' I said, still dreamily.

'Might be more cost effective to just bite the bullet and get it replaced now,' John continued. 'They'll deduct a couple of grand from your wages to pay for it obviously and a pig just flew past the window,' John was laughing now, and I was about to retort 'a couple of grand… they can't do that!' when I realised I was being played.

'Sorry, Luce, we sussed you and Paul out days ago. You couldn't have been more obvious if you'd tried!'

'Oh, I didn't realise,' was all I could say. John didn't seem shocked though, so maybe it was OK for people to know about us. It would certainly make life a whole lot easier.

Although Paul and I did rather rush our relationship, it seemed as though we were equally smitten. We were spending as much time together as possible and I was happy. Yes, I, Lucy Shaw, was happy. Paul made me smile. He was kind and funny, and a great dad who would tickle his adorable son out of a sulk. He was also absolutely amazing in bed. As much as I

72

had loved Dan, he'd never been all that good in the bedroom department. It hadn't mattered at the time, because my love for him really was blind. Sex with Paul, on the other hand, was a real eye-opener. He made me feel things that nobody ever had.

17

Self-analysis

Soon after I started going out with Paul, in mid-October, Carrie announced she was selling up and buying a one-bedroom flat. She needed to release some equity on the house. My heart sank at the news; I was so happy living with Carrie and suddenly my future was uncertain again.

'I'm so sorry, Lucy. If there was any other way, I'd have found it.' Carrie said, her hand squeezing my arm.

'Don't be daft! No need to apologise – can't be helped, life goes on and all that! It's not like you're moving to the other side of the world and we'll never see each other.' My usual reaction to receiving bad news – an outpouring of clichés to hide the hurt and protect the other person's feelings. What I really wanted to do was burst into tears and plead with Carrie to change her mind. Why didn't I do just that, I wondered? Show my real feelings, instead of hiding them behind a load of platitudes?

'I know, but it won't be the same, will it?' Carrie said, with a sad smile.

No, I thought to myself, wondering what on earth I was going to do. I'd been so happy living at Carrie's and felt pretty panicky about moving out. But did I say that? No, of course not, because I didn't want to make Carrie feel bad.

'It'll be fine, Carrie. An exciting new chapter for us both. As one door closes and all that!' Jeez, what was wrong with me? Clichés are us!

Swallowing back the ball of pain and tears that was growing in my throat, I gave Carrie a reassuring hug, and disappeared to my cellar-room to lick my wounds in private. As I sat on my bed, silent tears rolling down my cheeks (I couldn't even cry out loud in case Carrie heard), I wondered why I felt the need to keep such a stiff upper lip in the face of upset. I knew it was a very British way of behaving, but there must be more to it than that, I concluded. What had happened to make me this way?

I so wanted someone to talk to about the way I was feeling. I wanted to sob aloud and ask 'Why? Why was I so dysfunctional? Why couldn't I just release the flood of emotions welling up inside me?' I wished I felt closer to my sisters or my mum at that moment, and that I could confide in one of them, but they were all somehow so unsympathetic and judgmental. I often felt that they didn't really like me, which made me desperately sad. I didn't understand their attitudes when all I had ever done was try to keep everyone happy.

Maybe the time had come to try to break down the emotional barriers, I thought as I pulled a tissue from the box by my bed, wiping my eyes and blowing my nose. Plumping up the four pillows on my bed and making myself more comfortable, I opened my laptop and loaded Facebook. Before I chickened out, I private messaged middle sister Katie (I wasn't brave enough to pick up the phone):

'Hey sis. How're you? Hope all's well. I have news of the not so happy variety – got to find somewhere else to live.' I added a sad face and a kiss, and sat back with a sigh, hoping she'd get back to me quickly.

It was actually only a few minutes later that I got the ping of a reply from her:

'Oh no! That's pants! What are you going to do?'

'I don't know yet. Haven't stopped crying since I found out!' I wrote, hoping to initiate some sort of emotional dialogue.

'Something will turn up – it always does. You always land on your feet.'

There it was. That subtle little dig. Did I always land on my feet? I wondered.

'Do I? That's not how it feels to me right now.'

'Yeah, you're the sorted one of us, Luce. Nothing ever gets you down. Mum thinks you must be permanently drunk or something,' Katie replied.

'What?! You're joking, right?! I'm about as sorted as the Post Office at Christmas!'

'Well, you always seem so upbeat and happy. Life and soul and all that.'

'God, you couldn't be more wrong, Katie. It's all an act – a mask I put on around other people.'

'Bloody Nora! Really? You should have been an actress in that case. You deserve an Oscar! Are you seriously saying you're unhappy?'

'Well, yes. Not all the time, of course. But when I am, I don't want to bring anyone else down, so I put on my happy face and pretend everything's hunky dory in Lucy-land, when all I really want to do is sob and be comforted.'

'Blimey. I honestly never realised. That sounds exhausting.'

'It is. It's so draining, but I don't seem to be able to help it. I can't bear to make other people feel bad, so I pretend everything's rosy. Somehow I feel that it doesn't matter how unhappy

I am, as long as everyone else is OK.'

'You can't live like that, Luce. It's not healthy to bottle everything up. Why do you think you're like it?'

'I don't know,' I replied, adding a teary-eyed emoticon.

'Rose and I were chatting the other day about why we have the hang-ups we do. I think our upbringing has a lot to answer for.'

I felt my heart constrict a little at the mention of my eldest sister's name. More and more I had been feeling that she didn't like me. The fact that she and Katie were obviously closer, made me sad.

'Oh! Were you? How is Rose?' I said, once more hiding my hurt.

'She's muddling along as ever. Suffering from empty nest syndrome though now that her three have all flown the coop.'

'That must be hard. So, did the two of you come to any real conclusions about why we are the way we are?'

'Not really. Just that we could probably all use some therapy! Mum and Dad included!'

'I've always tried not to blame Mum and Dad for things – made excuses for them I suppose.'

(Our dad had been packed off to boarding school at the grand old age of seven, and Mum had found herself pregnant at seventeen, which was most definitely frowned upon in the early 1960s.)

'It's not about blame though, really, is it? It's about understanding,' Katie typed.

'I can't remember a time when I didn't have my 'happy' mask. I just want people to like me, to want to be around me and feel happy. Even people I don't really like, which is pretty screwed up, isn't it? Why am I like that?'

'Buggered if I know!' Katie replied.

'Some of my earliest memories are of Dad and his girlfriend after he and Mum split up. And of being careful not to say anything to upset Mum or 'her'. Not to mention one in front of the other. Of treading on eggshells around the grown-ups in our lives. Do you think that's why I'm like this now?'

'Could be, I suppose. Would make sense – a sort of learned behaviour that's become ingrained. I suppose we all did it, but you were that much younger.'

'I've always felt that I have to protect other people's feelings, whatever the cost to myself. It looks as though I've done too good a job!' I wrote, trying to make light of things.

'You've certainly been very convincing. Maybe you need to stop trying to please everyone else and work out what you want.'

'I'm sure you're right. I will try, but old habits die hard, Katie. I don't think it's going to be all that easy to change.'

'You won't know 'til you try. Maybe you should start by talking to Mum and Rose – they're living under the same misconceptions as me. Or maybe you should get drunk – Mum does love being right!'

'Ha! Thanks, Katie. I'll give it some thought. See you soon. Take care. X'

'You too, Lucy-Lou.'

I felt a bit better after my 'chat' with Katie, but, before I tackled my family problems, I had to address the issue of finding somewhere to live.

18

Temporary insanity

After the initial panic about what I was going to do, I heard that a friend of a friend was looking for someone to house share with in the town. When I say a friend of a friend, that was how he started out. I may have dated him very briefly for reasons I cannot explain or understand. I can only assume I was not in my right mind at the time and try to forget that it ever happened.

Anyway, it was agreed that Neil (nicknamed Short Camp by me and Carrie) and I would rent a house in Maidstone together. Problem solved. Or not. Problems just beginning methinks. What was I thinking? I had no idea. Clearly not a lot of thinking was going on in my brain at the time. Between the call of my ovaries and the panic over being homeless, I had no brain capacity left for sensible reasoning.

We did find a lovely big old house to rent in a pretty good location, and Neil and I set up camp along with his cat, Mr. D'Arcy, and his rabbit, Petal. (And, I suspect, a stash of Judy Garland movies.)

My friend Ali was a regular visitor to the house and would share Mr. D'Arcy's room, or should that be cell, when she stayed over. I have all too vivid memories of one such night when Ali and I were going to a colleague's leaving do. Ali was coming over early for a bite to eat and a few drinks before we went out and she rang me from her car asking me to guide her onto the drive which was a bit of a tight fit. Quickly checking the pizza which was cooking in the oven, I went out onto the drive to assist as best I could. Just as Ali got out of the car, the front door blew shut behind us. Oops. I had dashed out the front without thinking (no change there then, Lucy) and had no keys to get back in...

Short Camp was away overnight and the only other person with a key was the landlord. No problem, I thought, I'll phone him and plead with him to come to the rescue of a damsel in distress. The only flaw in this plan was that my mobile phone which contained the phone number was locked inside the house. Bugger. We needed a plan B. Having ascertained that we could not gain access to the house through any other door or window, I started to worry. Mainly about the pizza which would now be rather more crispy than it ought to be. Thank God Ali was there as she is the calmest and most practical person I know. Unfortunately, her practical skills did not extend to lock-picking. Despite her lack of burglary skills, Ali was not about to be beaten. This woman wasn't in the Territorial Army for nothing I'll have you know. (Apparently it was for the travel and social life.)

I was feeling particularly girly and pathetic by this time, and was also worried about what Short Camp and the Landlord would say when they saw that we had tried to force the back door. I wasn't going to be able to blame the screwdriver marks on Mr. D'Arcy or Petal either: they were on the wrong side of the door.

By now, a smell of burning was emanating from the kitchen. The pizza was being cremated and I had visions of it catching alight.

'Oh God,' I groaned, 'that would be just perfect, set the house on fire on top of everything else.'

'Well, look on the bright side,' said Ali, 'at least when the fire brigade arrives they can break the door down.'

Even the prospect of firemen didn't make me feel any better, however, and the situation was getting desperate. As was I. I really needed to pee.

'Ali,' I wailed, 'what are we going to do?'

That was Ali's cue to go all macho and come to my rescue. Now Ali's quite a big girl, a bit boyish-looking with her short hair. But she's fit. No, not like that, she's not my type. Sporty-fit. She plays rugby and jumps out of planes, cycles or runs to work, and does something called 'spinning' at the gym. (Don't ask me, I've no idea.) She said we'd have to break a window and suggested that the small pantry window would be the best bet; it was out of sight of the main road, would be easier and cheaper to replace than any of the others, and least likely to get noticed by Neil or the landlord.

By now I would have agreed to pretty much anything (no, not that Ali. No offence and all that but you're still not my type), so Ali set about smashing the window as quietly as possible. Hmm. A teeny bit of an oxymoron there methinks. All we needed was the neighbours hearing us trying to break into the house and calling the police. We'd just need one of us to cut ourselves on the glass and we'd have all the emergency services present. While the idea of even more men in uniform turning up on my doorstep was appealing, I pushed the thought to the back of my mind, and turned my attention back to Ali who was now trying to squeeze herself through the broken window.

It really was a very small window. And Ali really wasn't a very small person. By some miracle, however, and with only her clothes needing stitches, she somehow managed to wriggle herself through the opening and down into the pantry. Hurrah! She quickly unlocked the back door and let me in.

Thankfully, the pizza hadn't caught fire, but it was well and truly incinerated and completely inedible. This was not good news as we were now going to be drinking on empty stomachs. There simply wasn't time to get anything else to eat as we were already running terribly late due to my brainlessness.

My stupidity set the tone for the evening, and several vodkas later I found myself in the ladies' loo at Wetherspoons with my head down the toilet. I think they call it worshipping the porcelain God. Well, I wanted to die at this point, but my prayers went unanswered. I'd never been particularly religious, and this was obviously a false God. So I forsook my God and, in between technicolour yawns, could be heard crying pathetically that 'I just want Paul'. It was a miracle that he didn't deny all knowledge of me that night – I was in a right state, and we'd not been going out long. Was I really the sort of woman he wanted to bring into his young, impressionable son's life?

Yes, in a word. Apparently he did, and only four months into our relationship, on Valentine's Day, we got engaged and I moved in with him. And Jamie. The little baggage.

19

The easy way out

I carried on working initially, but Jamie was the perfect excuse to give up my job and, in March, to Paul's enthusiastic approval, I gave my three months' notice. Finally, all those months of planning on the escape committee which had been formed in my department came to fruition and I joined the lucky few who had successfully made it over the fence. I convinced myself that all I'd ever wanted was to be a housewife and mother and, at the age of thirty-six, settled into a routine of school runs and keeping house. I was sure that in no time I'd be wearing twin set and pearls and whipping up batches of muffins à la Stepford Wives. Well, as sure as I ever was about anything in life.

For a while, it felt as though I was simply on annual leave and I revelled in the freedom and enjoyed a relatively stress-free existence. Admittedly I soon missed my colleagues and the banter we used to share. We had been united by our hatred of our boss and I missed the camaraderie of the office. While Jamie was at school I had no-one for company except his two rabbits and they were pretty rubbish at conversation and didn't appreciate any of my jokes, not even my best rabbit joke:

A rabbit came into a shop and asked, 'Got any carrots?'
The shopkeeper answered, 'No.'

The next day the rabbit came again and asked, 'Got any carrots?'
The shopkeeper replied 'No!'
Next day the rabbit came and asked, 'Got any carrots?'
The shopkeeper shouted, 'No! And if you come again and ask for carrots, I'll take nails and hammer you to the wall by your ears!'
Early next morning the rabbit came back and asked, 'Got any nails?'
The seller answered, 'No!'
The rabbit asked, 'Got any carrots?'

I had been the life and soul of the office and suddenly there was no-one to laugh with (or at) or go to the pub with at lunch time. I was no longer part of the group and soon started to feel a bit excluded. I guess my job had also been my social life. I missed the human contact.

I consoled myself with the knowledge that I would never have to do another audit of the scary Sales and Marketing department, (the acronym for this department is no accident, heavy emphasis on the sado), or chair a meeting in a room full of scientific types talking about stuff I didn't understand. Let's be honest, it was only a matter of time before they sussed me out as a complete fraud at work and booted me out. I'd had a lucky escape and should count my blessings. One, another one, some, lots, too many to count – that's about the only thing I ever learnt in those microbiology meetings I never understood.

Thankfully, Jamie took to having me around without a problem and we soon grew close. He would sneak into our bed at night and snuggle up to me. I called him my little koala bear. I was kidding myself that we could continue on like that indefinitely as, ultimately, his mum would expect him to go and live with her and his little brother. For a while though we were a tight little family unit and we were happy.

The beginning of the end came when Jamie's mum promised him a trip to Florida's Disney World if he moved in with her and brother Scott, who was three at the time. We couldn't compete with Disney World in a five-year-old's mind. We couldn't afford to either, as Paul's house was up for sale by then to pay for his divorce.

Paul was sure that living with his mum was not the best thing for Jamie. I wasn't so convinced. Coming from a fractured family myself, I couldn't help thinking that it had to be best for the brothers to be together. I could not have imagined growing up without my sisters. Paul and I had endless discussions about Jamie's future:

'Lucy, you don't know Jamie's mum. She doesn't really care about what's best for Jamie – just what people might think of her son not wanting to live with her, and the financial implications – child maintenance payments and stuff.'

'But he should be with Scott. I know what's it's like to come from a broken home and I can't begin to imagine what it would have been like to grow up apart from my sisters.'

And so, we argued back and forth, neither of us budging, while all Jamie could think about was a trip to Disney. In reality Jamie's mum had already won, but Paul refused to give him up without a fight and it was left to the courts to make the decision about who Jamie should live with.

'I'm so sorry, Paul,' I tried to console as we left the court after the judge had given his ruling a few short weeks later.

'It's not right, Lucy. Jamie would be better off with me. I have no doubt about that, in my head or in my heart.' I could hear the break in his voice. He was devastated at the prospect of only seeing his beloved Jamie every other weekend, when he would visit with his younger brother.

After Jamie had moved out in late July, it was a novelty being just the two of us. We hadn't had a 'normal' courtship and it could have been a pretty special time if I hadn't started feeling dreadful at around the same time.

20

Puppy Love

I was permanently exhausted, piling on weight, and my brain definitely wasn't firing on all cylinders. My skin and hair were dull and lifeless and I was utterly miserable. I always had a headache and was regularly experiencing horrendous night sweats. So, I took myself off to my GP hoping for a miracle cure. The doctor listened patiently, passed me a box of tissues when I started to blub, and then suggested I have a blood test as it sounded as though I may have started the menopause early. Early? He wasn't kidding. I was only thirty-six and what was more I hadn't answered the call of my ovaries yet. He said we'd discuss things further after the blood test results came back. Too bloody right we would, I thought.

The wait for the results was an anxious one and the more I thought about it the more I worried. Paul and I hadn't been taking any precautions against conceiving but still nothing had happened. I hadn't been too bothered about things before, but the prospect of not being able to ever have a baby terrified me. I had always believed that I would one day be a mother. As I scrambled some eggs for breakfast the morning I was due to see the doctor again I thought of the old proverb not to count your chickens 'til they're hatched. At this rate I wouldn't be hatching anything. And they say you shouldn't put all your eggs in one basket don't they? Well I'm buggered if I'm going to use somebody else's basket. I didn't think surrogacy would be the answer for me. As I whisked the eggs in the bowl I wondered if it was a bad omen and that they weren't the only eggs that were about to be scrambled.

At the appointed hour I awaited my fate outside the GP's room. I absentmindedly picked up a magazine to pass the time. Nice one Lucy, I thought when I realised I'd just opened a copy of *Mother and Baby* at an article entitled 'How to have an enjoyable pregnancy'. Bastards. I'd settle for any pregnancy, enjoyable or not. I put the magazine down with a sigh and picked up a copy of *Fly Fishing*. That should be safe enough reading territory I figured. Just as I was reading about the inevitable 'one that got away' (true of things other than fish I mused, as Dan flashed into my mind), I heard my name over the tannoy and went in to face my fears.

Ten minutes later I left the surgery with a prescription for HRT, an appointment to see a specialist and the words 'your chances of having a baby are very slim' ringing in my ears. If I'd been featured in the fishing magazine in the waiting room, I would have been entitled 'stunned mullet'. I got back to my car and tried to let the news sink in. I rang Paul and my mum to tell them the news. Paul was stoical as ever (easy for him with two children to his name already, I thought nastily) but my mum was really upset at the thought of never having any little Lucies running around.

As I drove to the chemist I tried to be fatalistic about the whole thing, but I couldn't help feeling that life had dealt me a cruel blow. Certainly more than enough to stun a very large mullet.

'If I can't have a baby I want a puppy,' I announced suddenly.

It was now late August, a few weeks since I'd had my diagnosis, and Paul and I were lying in bed watching late night television. I still wasn't feeling great but assumed that I just needed to give the Hormone Replacement Therapy (or Hateful Reality Tablets) more time. 'Now that I've given up work, there's no reason why we couldn't have a dog,' I reasoned. I didn't need to persuade Paul – he would have done anything to make me happy. And shut me up.

The next day I scoured the local papers and pet shop windows to find out about any puppies for sale. I'd thought about rescue centres and all the poor, unwanted dogs that needed new homes but this wasn't about doing something worthy or charitable. This was about me needing something to channel all my maternal affection into. Let's be honest, this puppy was going to be my baby. This puppy was going to fill the void, to give my life new meaning. To complete me. Poor little sod had an awful lot to live up to.

Bingo! I found an advert for a litter of Springer Spaniel puppies ready to leave their (biological) mother the very next day. I told Paul about them and he agreed that I could phone up and enquire about the pups and make an appointment to go and see them. As I popped my HRT tablet in my mouth the next morning I felt like a new woman. (By this time Paul probably did too.) But it wasn't the hormones that were making the difference, it was the prospect of having a small helpless ball of fluff who needed me, and who would love me unconditionally. I was going to be a mummy. And I couldn't wait.

'Now remember,' Paul said as we pulled up outside the address the breeder had given me, 'we're only going to look today. OK?'

'Yes, yes, I know,' I replied automatically as I whipped off my seatbelt and sprang from the car. I rang the doorbell, heart in my mouth and soon we were being shown through to the kitchen where five adorable liver and white puppies were playing tug of war with a chew toy. Paul looked at me with an expression of resignation on his face. He knew full well we'd be leaving with one of these gorgeous little creatures that day.

We christened him Pippin and he was the apple of my eye.

'Bloody dog!' I screamed for the second time in as many minutes. Pippin had run off with yet another tea towel and was now sitting in the middle of the lawn waiting for me to chase him in a vain attempt to retrieve the trophy he'd taken from the kitchen. I knew he only wanted to play and that stealing something was the best way to get my attention, but he was driving me round the bloody bend. And God knows I was half way round before he even arrived on the scene. I knew that if I ignored him he would simply keep pinching things until I gave in and chased him round the garden. Might as well get it over with I decided and set off in pursuit of my very springy spaniel.

Pippin would wait until I was almost on top of him and then bound away an instant before I could grab him. What a good game. I think it was probably the dog equivalent of baby drops spoon, mummy picks up spoon, baby drops spoon… and so on. Terribly amusing for the baby/dog, but just infuriating for the parent. Eventually Pippin would get tired of winding me up and would agree to swap the tea towel for a dog biscuit. Like a baby, Pippin was very good at keeping me supplied with dirty washing. Admittedly I didn't have to change any nappies for this particular offspring, but that might have been preferable to scooping poop off the lawn. He also seemed to have just as many toys as a human baby and demanded just as much attention. But then I suppose that was why I'd got him in the first place; to fill the gaping baby-shaped hole in my life. Had I been wrong all along about a 'baby' being the answer to the question of my happiness?

We also had a bad case of sibling rivalry going on in the house. We already had our cat, Marmite, when Pippin came along. I foolishly believed that Pippin would accept Marmite as one of the family, and I was confident that Marmite would be totally cool about having a dog around as she'd shown no fear when my old retriever Jasper had come to visit. How wrong was I? Somewhere between very and horribly, horribly. Pippin went absolutely berserk every time he clapped eyes on Marmite and she naturally responded by hating his intrusion on her previously calm existence. Given the opportunity I think they would have fought like cat and dog. As a result of this mutual hatred we had to insert baby stair gates in doorways to segregate the warring factions and a great deal of stress was experienced by all parties in the efforts to keep the two of them apart. Maybe things would improve with time.

Pah! Things went from bad to worse and when we moved house we had to install an upstairs cat flap which would allow Marmite to get out onto a flat roof from where she could jump down onto a fence and so make her escape to the garden. Talk about upstairs and downstairs. Pippin was not allowed to venture out of the servants' quarters for fear of upsetting the more gentile folk upstairs. I'd like to say that peace broke out, but I'm afraid Pippin had other ideas. He decided to up the ante by getting into the guinea pig run and taking my sister's beloved guinea pig, who was staying with us while she was away, for a spin round the garden in his mouth. I don't think this was the sort of holiday excursion the guinea pig was expecting; it certainly hadn't said anything about it in the brochure. Thankfully, Pippin didn't hurt the poor creature, and by some miracle it didn't die from the shock of its little adventure.

Pippin also discovered the joys of chasing young rabbits when I took him out for walks. Unfortunately for the rabbits, he turned out to be a dab paw at catching them. What was more, he found out that he liked the taste of rabbit and could often be seen with just a pair of legs sticking out of his mouth as he woofed one down whole. When it first happened I tried to persuade him to swap the rabbit in his mouth for one of the bribing biscuits I always carried in my pocket. He wasn't, however, falling for the rabbit being a very furry tea towel, and my efforts were futile. After that I just had to let him get on with his one dog mission to rid the world of lovely fluffy bunnies.

For all his doggy ways, Pippin did have his good points. He made me go out walking twice a day whatever the weather, and he took my mind off my menopausal misery. He was a willing receptacle for all the love I had to give and in return he loved me unconditionally. Even when I shouted at him for the umpteenth time that day. Just like a child he drove me up the wall a lot of the time, but then he'd look at me with his big brown puppy dog eyes and my heart would melt. It was impossible to stay angry with him for long. He was the most adorable little thing. And I loved the little sod.

I didn't love him quite so much when he stopped coming to me when I called him. We would be out for a walk and he would be on the scent of something, or just not want to go home, and I would find myself unable to get him back on the lead. He would come back when he was good and ready and I would have my work cut out trying to get hold of his collar before he ran out on the road. Then, when I managed to get him into the boot of the car, he would leap out again just as I lowered the door. So much for walking being good for your health. I was in danger of having a nervous breakdown every time I took Pippin out. What made it even more frustrating was that he was the star pupil at his training classes and did everything that was asked of him. Talk about teacher's pet. But the minute he was out of the classroom he turned into a disobedient little bugger. Parenthood was tougher than I'd expected, and I didn't think a sticker chart was going to be the answer in this case. I needed the dog equivalent of Supernanny, but I settled for a weekend away with the girls.

21

Pilgrimage to Bognor

I'd been looking forward to my weekend away with the girls for ages. Pippin hadn't proved to be the salve I had hoped, my thirty-seventh birthday had come and gone in a hor-moan-al blur, and I desperately needed to get away from it all. We were heading off to Butlin's in Bognor Regis for a three-night 'Disco Inferno' in early December. It was just what the doctor ordered (along with the HRT) after a stressful few months. Paul assured me he could look after Pippin and I couldn't wait to be free of any responsibility for a few days. It wasn't the first time we'd gone to one of these adult only themed music weekends at Butlin's. I must confess I was a little worried about what people might think the first time we went, but we'd had such a good time and laughed so much that I no longer cared. So it wasn't five-star luxury at a health spa, but it did us every bit as much good. Admittedly I usually needed a stay at a five-star luxury health spa to recover afterwards, but it was worth it.

I was making this annual pilgrimage to Bognor with two former work colleagues: Ali, of the breaking and entering/burnt pizza episode, and Sue. Ali was great company and up for anything and Sue just loved to dance. I guess I was somewhere between the two: not quite as fearless as Ali and definitely not as good a dancer as Sue. But the mix of personalities worked and we rarely fell out over anything. That may have had something to do with the fact that we never fancied the same men. Of course on this trip I would only be looking and not touching because I was no longer single.

During the drive down to Sussex, we reminisced about our first Butlin's weekend two years previously. We'd been to a couple of the over eighteen music weekends held at Butlin's in the quiet winter season. Back then, I was single and Ali and Sue were both in unhappy marriages, so we were all up for a bit of a laugh and eager to get away from real life for a bit. A bit of what I hear you ask? Well, that's for me to know. What happens at Butlin's stays at Butlin's. (You have to imagine that said with a wink.) Anyway, that first time was an absolute scream.

That December weekend, two years earlier, after we'd eventually located our particular chalet in the warren of identical chalets, we'd quickly unpacked our bags (the one containing the vodka first if I remember rightly) and put on a disco CD to get the party started. The rooms were basic to say the least, but the heater worked and we didn't really care about anything except a mirror for putting our make-up on and a bed to collapse on at the end of the night. Collapse was the operative word here and I had to put my case under the bed to keep my bum off the floor. All meals were included in the weekend and the food, like the room, was basic but satisfactory. It lined our stomachs which was all we really needed.

When we'd made our way to the venue later that night, we were already feeling slightly squiffy.

'I have to say, ladies, I'm feeling a bit iffy,' I'd remarked to Ali and Sue as we walked.

'Probably the dodgy dinner, Luce,' Ali had laughed.

'Absolutely,' agreed Sue. 'Nothing whatsoever to do with the booze!'

I think it must have been the slightly dubious holiday camp food, but the vodka may have been a contributing factor, I supposed. Anyway, we were ready to let our hair, and our standards, down and have a good time. The evening had started with some disco tribute bands to set the mood for the night, and we found ourselves a table with a good view of both stage and bar to ensure we didn't miss the talent on stage or off.

It had soon become apparent that fancy dress was encouraged at these events, and the room rapidly filled up with guys in afros and satin shirts, and groups of girls in very short nurses' uniforms. It wasn't long before I saw a group of eligible-looking 'doctors' arrive.

'Ooh, talent at ten o'clock,' I said, giving Ali a nudge with my elbow.

'Roger that,' grinned Ali.

As I turned to Sue, to make sure she had spotted the group of men at the bar, she was looking at her watch.

'But it's only eight-forty-five now. That's ages away,' she said sounding rather despondent. Sue wasn't the sharpest knife in the drawer.

'D'oh! Not as in time, silly! Think direction – ten o'clock is over to our left, at the bar,' I explained.

'Oh! I see,' Sue said, but I wasn't convinced she had the faintest idea what I was talking about.

'It looks like that group of nurses is headed their way, Luce,' Ali warned.

'Oh no you don't, I saw them first. Let's go!' I was already on my feet and ready to do battle.

We were smooth operators, and pretty nimble on our feet when required. Slamming on the brakes just before we reached the bar, and just ahead of the competition, we tried to look ultra-casual. Unfortunately, the sprint had rather taken it out of us and we ended up looking in need of medical attention. Is there a doctor in the house?

We soon got chatting to the men in white coats (ha ha, stop making your own jokes) and discovered they were really an assortment of policemen and electricians from the West Midlands. I'd wondered briefly if I could cope with the Brummie accent, but they seemed like a nice group of blokes, so we decided to stick around. Along with their white coats and stethoscopes, all the 'doctors' were wearing name badges: Drs Ben Dover and Phil McAvity are two that I remember well. Along with the inevitable 'Dicks': Head and Fitzwell and a couple of 'Hughs': Hugh G. Rection and Hugh Jass. Their comedy names were a great ice-breaker and soon sparked a discussion on suitable names for lady doctors. I ended up as Norma Snockers, Ali was Jean Poole, and Sue was Mona Lott, having discounted Marsha Mellow and Hazel Nutt. We laughed a lot that night. Those guys were a real tonic, and just what the doctor ordered.

The following morning, we were all, unsurprisingly, feeling rather fragile. 'I think I've got food poisoning,' Sue had moaned pathetically as she joined me and Ali in the kitchen area of the chalet.

'You and me both,' I'd agreed, leaning on the breakfast bar, with my head in my hands.

'What a pair of lightweights you two are,' Ali had laughed. 'A couple of drinks and look at the state of you.'

'This is no laughing matter, Alison, we may actually have alcohol poisoning.' Even then, I only called Ali by her full name when pretending to be cross with her.

'Don't worry, nothing a good old fry-up won't fix,' Ali had replied.

After a somewhat half-hearted full-English, we had decided to walk into town and see what Bognor's shops had to offer (not a lot as it turned out), and the bracing walk along the seafront helped clear our heads a bit. We'd still been feeling, and looking, pretty ropey, however, and were not thrilled when we spotted the group of guys from the night before. We'd ducked into the nearest shop (which regrettably turned out to be an Age Concern charity shop) and hoped they hadn't seen us, or at least hadn't recognised us as the gorgeous creatures from the bar. (I would later have to re-think this statement when I saw the photos of me looking red-faced, sweaty and drunk as a skunk.)

We'd spent the rest of that weekend two years previously drinking and dancing our cares away. That was the weekend that set the Butlin's standard and had us vowing to return once a year for more of the same. Except it never was quite the same after that. I guess it's always a mistake to try and repeat something so successful, but we weren't willing to give up just yet, hence I found myself once more en-route to Bognor, wondering what this weekend would throw up. Other than dinner.

Either I was getting old, or I was coming down with something, but I really wasn't up to much that weekend, two years after the last one. I felt so tired that I even changed into jeans and trainers halfway through the night when my high heels got the better of me. Oh dear, standards were slipping. I didn't care what anyone thought: I just needed to be comfortable or I wasn't going to go the distance. We had fun, but neither I nor Butlin's really sparkled this time and I was relieved to get home, crawl into my own bed and sleep off the exhaustion.

22

The Bognor Miracle

Two weeks later I was still feeling hung-over. I was obviously more run down than I'd realised but this was getting ridiculous. And of course, Pippin still needed walking and the house needed cleaning, meals had to be cooked and shirts ironed. I bought myself a tonic from the chemist to try and give myself a boost and overdosed on friendly bacteria yoghurt drinks to no avail. I'd also missed a period but thought nothing of this as I believed I was in the menopause and assumed the HRT was messing with my hormones. I don't know what made me do it, but I found myself buying my first ever pregnancy test and weeing on a stick while Paul was at work, not believing for a moment that I could actually be pregnant. The test was positive, but I still didn't believe it and decided to repeat the process when Paul got home that night. I was hovering by the front door when he walked in.

'Hello. How was your day? I think I might be pregnant,' I yabbered before he was even through the door.

'Hi, good thanks. You what?!' I don't think Paul's ears had been able to keep up and process my words.

'I think I'm pregnant,' I repeated, more slowly.

'Oh, ha ha, very funny, Luce. What's for dinner?' Paul really thought I was joking.

'Dinner? Do you really think I've been able to think about

dinner since I peed on the stick-thing?' I think I may have sounded a little hysterical.

'Oh my God! You're serious? Really?'

'Yes, really. I did a pregnancy test and it was positive.' I could hear the disbelief in my own voice. 'I was waiting for you to get home before repeating the test - I still can't quite believe it.'

'Do it now! Lucy, this is amazing!' Paul sounded overjoyed.

By now, Paul had closed the front door behind him and dumped his coat and laptop bag in the hall. Taking my hand, he pulled me towards the downstairs loo, opening the door for me, and pushing me gently into the room. I had become a bit zombie-like at this point.

'Right, where's the test kit?' Paul was so calm and together. As he said this, he spotted the pee stick next to the sink, and put it into my hand. 'Do your thing and I'll be right outside,' he said.

I did my thing and then re-joined Paul who was waiting expectantly just outside the loo. I half expected to see a cigar in his hand. That would have been a bit premature. The three-minute wait felt more like three hours, but the result was the same as the first test.

Holy hell. I was pregnant. I would have to get in touch with the Vatican as a matter of urgency and get Bognor on the miracle map. Paul was so excited, more for me than for himself. After all, he had already fathered Jamie and Scott and it wasn't such a big deal for him.

Once the pregnancy had been confirmed by my GP, I wandered about in a bit of a daze. How could I have a baby when I already had a spaniel puppy with the canine equivalent of Attention Deficit Hyperactivity Disorder? I was torn between being thrilled to be having a baby when the doctors had told me it just wasn't going to happen and wondering how the hell I was going to cope. Sodding Sod's Law in action again. Get a dog because I can't have a baby and lo and behold I'm pregnant. I don't know why I was so surprised. How many times had I heard of women who'd given up hope of ever having a baby and promptly finding themselves pregnant? Lots. Well, alright, a few. But it's like that saying, 'a watched pot never boils' isn't it? Take your eye off it for a minute, however, and the bloody thing boils over. Well, I had well and truly boiled over.

I tried hard to keep a lid on the boiling pot of my pregnancy until I was safely through the first twelve weeks, but was rubbish at keeping secrets and had soon told close friends and family. I knew how thrilled my mum would be and just had to tell her. Everyone was so pleased for us and I gradually started to enjoy my pregnancy and the prospect of being a mum. As for Pippin, he would be nine months older by the time the baby arrived and was bound to have calmed down. Everything would work out fine. Hurrah!

I think as pregnancies go, mine was relatively good. I didn't have major morning sickness, and what I did suffer was eased with ginger biscuits and ginger ale. (With only a moment's worry that this might lead to a ginger baby.) My blood pressure hovered around the top end of normal, which was entirely normal for me. And, best of all, I didn't blow up like a barrage balloon. I was all bump and boobs, but from the back I didn't look too bad. I blossomed as only a pregnant lady can, with glossy hair and bright eyes. I only needed a wet nose and I could have given Pippin a run for his money. The only blip came at sixteen weeks when a blood test showed a very high risk of Downs syndrome. After much agonising I underwent an agonising amniocentesis to determine if my baby did indeed have Downs. I never want to see a needle that big again. Unless I'm learning how to knit. (Which I have to say is highly unlikely.) I can still remember getting the call to say the baby was fine, which came after an even more agonising wait. In a nutshell, it was an agonising time. I just thank God I didn't have to make a decision about whether or not to end the pregnancy as that would have been… yes, you guessed it… agonising.

I was absolutely convinced I was having a girl, and I'd already chosen a name for my daughter. The only reason I believed this was that I was told I would have one child and it would be a girl, by a woman who did me a tarot card reading a year or so earlier. Sounds bonkers now, but I was utterly convinced I'd have a girl. I hadn't planned to find out the sex of the baby before the birth, but decided that I would like to know following the amniocentesis. Paul just went along with whatever I wanted, and we were given the news that the baby was a boy. After a brief feeling of disappointment I quickly accepted the news and adapted my thinking accordingly. To be honest, I was so relieved that my baby was healthy that the sex was no longer important. In more ways than one. Sorry Paul. I'd gone right off the boil by then.

When I finally reached forty weeks I was fed up with being pregnant. It was August and I couldn't get cool or comfortable. Pippin still wouldn't accept Marmite and continued to drive us round the bend. He was still a nightmare to take for walks and showing no sign of calming down. He'd graduated from dog-training with flying colours, but what he'd learned in class didn't seem to translate into real life. I tried not to think about how I was going to cope with him and a new baby, when just getting through the barricades to go upstairs was a struggle. Anyway, I'd had other things to worry about. Like giving birth.

Even as a young girl I'd had a pronounced fear of childbirth. I knew my mum had a tough time giving birth to Rose who was breach, and had nearly died from haemorrhaging when she had me. I tried to rationalise childbirth as something completely natural that millions of women do every day, but to be honest I was crapping myself. Yes, and apparently that's one thing I might have no control of during labour. Oh deep joy and endless humiliation.

It seemed, however, that baby was in no hurry to arrive. The doctors had other ideas when my blood pressure started rising and other signs of pre-eclampsia appeared, and they decided to induce me. Well, they could induce me all they liked, but my baby and I had other ideas and clung on to each other limpet-like. Even the agony of contractions every two minutes didn't make me anymore cooperative and I positively refused to dilate anything except my pupils. To cut a very long, and rather gruesome, story short, Tom was finally delivered by emergency caesarean section at 11:57 p.m. on August thirteenth. He'd just made it in time to be a Friday the thirteenth baby. Seemed only fitting as my birthday is on Halloween.

My lasting memories of labour were having to let Paul take me for a wee (I'd never gone to the loo in front of any previous boyfriends), enjoying gas and air immensely, and throwing up a lot when they took me to theatre for surgery. I felt a little cheated that I didn't get to experience real childbirth and the whole pushing bit, but friends have since assured me that it's highly over-rated and to be thankful I didn't have to be cut and stitched up *down there*. No, but I did have to be cut and stitched across my bikini line and would not only be trying to recover from emergency surgery, but coping with a new baby and a crazy Springer spaniel who would still expect to be walked twice a day. It was not a recipe for success.

I have to confess that I didn't enjoy my first days in hospital with my new baby son. The emergency surgery meant that I had a catheter in and had to wear those hideous stockings that prevent thrombosis. Bearing in mind it was the middle of August and, for a change, was incredibly hot, it was not a comfortable experience. To make matters worse, I was completely hopeless at breast feeding - I just couldn't get Tom to latch on, and every nurse or midwife I saw gave me different advice. Personally I think it was a simple case of too much boob and not enough nipple. My cup size had gone up to an 'L' by then and that's an 'ell of a big boob let me tell you.

Tom was also pretty dopey for the first couple of days. I'd had that many drugs during labour that he was still a bit out of it. To add to the joys of new-motherhood, I had to express milk (ouch) and get Tom to sip it from a cup. They wouldn't let me give him a bottle in case he was then unable to ever get the hang of breast feeding. At this point I didn't think I'd ever get the hang of it myself. In an attempt to get 'mother and baby to bond' they had us doing 'Kangaroo care'. (Well, I'd got the pouch now I mused.) This turned out to be skin-to-skin contact. It worked. The amount of sweat created bonded us alright. Like glue.

On the plus side, because of the surgery, I wasn't expected to bath Tom myself which was a relief. I could just imagine doing it all wrong and being told off by the midwife, then dropping the slippery little sod. They'd have been on the phone to Social Services in a flash, shouting 'unfit mother' to anyone who'd listen. To be honest I felt like an unfit mother at this stage. I felt utterly miserable and terribly alone. Not to mention scared witless.

So, it was with more than a little trepidation that I left the hospital. I was relieved to be leaving but still incredibly anxious about coping at home. My anxiety wasn't helped by the fact that I nearly passed out when I reached the car. They didn't give me a wheelchair - I think the theory was that if I was well enough to go home then I was well enough to walk to the car. It didn't bode well, but at least Paul had a few days leave to help out.

The first six weeks were pretty hellish as my wound refused to heal and became infected. I couldn't lift anything, couldn't drive, couldn't do most things in fact. At least Tom and I had got the hang of breast feeding though, which was a relief as it meant no faffing around with bottles and sterilisers.

Two courses of antibiotics later and I was starting to feel vaguely human again. That's about the time that Tom developed evening colic and screamed from around six o'clock in the evening until midnight/1 a.m. The doctor advised us as to what medicine was available and reassured us that the colic would probably go after about three months. When you're suffering from sleep deprivation and having to endure the heart-rending cries of your baby, three months sounds like an eternity. It felt like one too, and Paul and I would sit on the bed night after night, trying to hold it together and taking it in turns to walk around with Tom and rub his tummy. I can honestly say that there were times when I wished that I had never got pregnant. It was a dark, despairing time and the light at the end of the tunnel had definitely blown a bulb.

Sure enough though, when Tom was three-and-a-half months old, the colic stopped. The relief was immense and I hoped I would now be able to start enjoying motherhood. I also stopped breast feeding at this time. I'd had my fill of sitting in car parks (in the car obviously) feeding Tom. I'd never been comfortable whipping my boobs out in public places (people might have thought there was an eclipse) and I wanted to start feeling that my body belonged to me again. I was never going to be one of those earth mothers who breast feed their children until they're three and whip their saggy tits out left, right and centre (well, left and right, unless they're the amazing three-tittied woman) but I hoped that I had given Tom a good start and a strong immune system. (Had I heck, as I was to discover later.)

23

Millstones and milestones

The only real blot that remained on the landscape was Pippin, who hadn't calmed down and was the cause of a great deal of stress. We were now living in the middle of nowhere in a village on the outskirts of Maidstone; there were no pavements and the footpaths were impassable with a pram. I couldn't carry Tom any distance due to my op and the bad back I suffered due to the weight of my chest, and walking Pippin became virtually impossible. It just wasn't fair on him but we couldn't bear the thought of re-homing him. It couldn't be denied, however, that the combination of baby and dog was a nightmare. Something had to give. That was when Paul's mum and dad came to the rescue and offered to take him on. I'd miss Tom, but we just couldn't go on as we were. Only joking. Sort of. On a serious note, I was heartbroken saying goodbye to Pippin, but I knew he was going to a good home and at least we'd still be able to see him. He'd always adored Paul's dad anyway, so I wasn't worried for him. I was more worried about how John and Margaret, who were no spring chickens, would cope with our crazy hound. I just hoped they had a plentiful supply of tea towels and the patience of saints.

Although I felt guilty about giving up Pippin, I was also incredibly relieved. An air of relative calm descended on the household, and Marmite heaved a sigh of relief when she realised Pippin wasn't coming back. Life was going to be so much easier from now on.

Well, yes, it was easier, relatively speaking. Apart from Tom's terrible teething. None of Tom's teeth came easily and he seemed to get every possible side effect. The worst of these was the diarrhoea. They hadn't invented a nappy that could withstand the force or quantity of my son's bodily waste and I got into the habit of carrying copious amounts of wipes, nappies, nappy sacks, disinfectant, sanitizing hand gel and spare clothes with me at all times.

There are so many milestones in a child's life and I tried to mark them in as permanent a fashion as possible by making him a scrap book to act as a reminder in later life. I dutifully saved bits and bobs from birthday parties and other special occasions and printed photos which were cut and pasted against imaginative backgrounds in what I hoped was an aesthetically pleasing fashion. For example, his first birthday page includes a Bob the Builder serviette and a photograph of a Thomas the Tank Engine cake. I was really quite proud of myself for doing something a proper mummy would do. The fact that after a while I couldn't really be arsed to do the scrapbook and now have a big bag full of 'bits' to stick in at a later date is irrelevant. After all, it's the thought that counts, and I really am a very thoughtful person.

However, of the many pages I had managed to complete, one of my favourites was from Tom's time at Nursery School, which he'd started attending a couple of mornings a week from the age of two. It was tough leaving him the first few times, especially when he cried and clung on to me like a little koala bear, begging me not to go. He really tore at my heartstrings and I felt like I was drowning kittens. As it turned out, he was absolutely fine the minute I was out of sight, the manipulative little sod. I don't know about tugging at my heartstrings – Tom was an accomplished puppet master at the age of two. I had to be strong though as I knew I would be a better mum if I had a break from him now and then. Mind you, by the time I'd got home from dropping him off, put some washing in and done a couple of bits in the house, it was time to go and collect him again. But it was better than nothing. As long as I could harden my heart to the kitten-drowning bit when I dropped him off.

Also featured on this scrapbook page was Tom's first Nativity Play, in which he was an owl. Between us Paul and I managed to concoct him an owl outfit from brown fabric and cardboard and we made sure the camera was charged so that we could record this milestone in a little boy's life. Unfortunately, on the day of the play, Tom was ill and I have never seen a more pitiful owl in my life. If the RSPB had been there they would have rushed him to a vet. The poor little thing had one of his many ear infections and the antibiotics had upset his tummy. Looking back I don't know why we let him attend that day. I guess we figured if his bottom exploded, at least it wouldn't show. Maybe if he'd been dressed in white, he'd have got to stay home that day. Anyway, he did go and he spent the entire performance sitting on one of the helper's laps, looking so sad and ill that the guilt will probably never leave me. When I'm not feeling guilty about that day, I'm always reminded of that joke about the difference between a bad marksman and a constipated owl. You know, one shoots and can't hit…

Nursery school was also our first experience of sports day, which I fear will never be one of my favourite days in the school calendar. Tom was not a natural athlete and I found myself feeling uncomfortable watching him compete and never win. My heart went out to him as I knew how upset he would be, and all I wanted to do was protect him from defeat and failure and the big bad world. I knew I had to let him try, and sometimes fail, but it broke my heart to see him upset. I tried to say all the right things to him; how it's not the winning but the taking part and as long as he did his best that was all that mattered etc. etc. But, when you're little, winning is everything.

I didn't only dread sports day for Tom's sake. I lived in fear of having to take part in a parents' race. As any large-breasted woman will tell you, running is not a pleasant experience, either physically or emotionally. The thought of my massive mammaries bouncing up and down in front of all those other parents was not a happy one. But how could I justify not taking part to my two-year-old son who'd just done his best to wheel a barrow round an obstacle course and lost a running race to a girl half his size? How could I tell him one minute that it's the taking part which is important and then refuse to do so myself? So that's why I found myself running up the field in the three-legged race, with Paul tied up next to me (well, at least he was happy) and my arms folded across my chest to minimise bounce. I hoped Tom would be proud of us for at least having a go. And we only bloody well won. Come on you losers!

Another of the early pages in Tom's memory book was his parents' wedding day. I know you're not supposed to be at your parents' wedding but this was not a conventional wedding in any sense. Paul and I had both been married before and just wanted a quiet wedding. To be honest, the main reason for marrying was that I hated having a different surname to Tom.

I could remember how I'd felt when my mum had remarried and changed her last name and I hadn't liked it one little bit.

We only invited our parents, Paul's sons Jamie and Scott, and a friend each to act as our witnesses. I didn't even buy a new outfit or get my hair done as we needed the money to pay for a holiday. It was a pretty informal ceremony in the Registry Office in Maidstone and the image of Scott doing a handstand halfway through will never leave me. For our reception, we'd booked a table at a nearby family restaurant that had a play area for the boys. No fuss, no cake, no speeches. Just a new name for me and a change of tax code for Paul.

Our 'honeymoon' was actually a week in the Canaries which we'd booked before deciding to get married. Having a toddler with us pretty much put paid to any romantic plans Paul had and we spent our evenings playing Scrabble in the room while Tom slept in the cot next to our bed. In the absence of bromide, I made sure I didn't play any Scrabble words of a sexual nature. In one round I could have used all seven letters, but there was no way I was putting down the word 'BLOWJOB'. Besides, I didn't even know for sure if it was one word or two.

When we returned from honeymoon, we settled back into some semblance of a routine. Well, Paul did as he went back to work. Tom and I just muddled through the days as best we could. I was pretty useless as a mum to be honest. I think I resented not being able to do whatever I wanted, whenever I wanted. That's the trouble with being an older mum: you're more mature and able to cope emotionally with the demands of bringing up a child, but you've had more time to become selfish. Suddenly having this other person who is completely dependent on you, and extremely demanding with it, is one hell of a shock. Much as I loved Tom, there were times – I'm ashamed to say – when I wished he had remained a twinkle in his daddy's eye.

Of course, there were wonderful moments which I will cherish. When Tom said his first word, for example. Thankfully it was 'mum' and not some choice swear word he'd picked up when I'd had a teensy case of road rage. Since having Tom, I did try very hard to restrain myself when confronted with bad drivers, but just occasionally I did slip and could be seen gesticulating wildly at another motorist while shouting obscenities. I could just imagine turning up at mothers and toddlers and Tom toddling round the room shouting 'TW*T' at the top of his voice.

Tom was walking at ten months and seemed to do everything pretty early. Waking up especially. Another problem with being an older parent – we don't have the energy of younger mums and dads, and take longer to recover after exertion. (Another reason not to have sex methinks, mentally adding it to my arsenal. As a Spurs supporter, Paul didn't stand a chance.)

I may have been a useless parent, but I was also a very proud one. All of Tom's achievements and his obvious eligibility for MENSA gave me great pleasure. I was proud as punch when he started talking in sentences before any of the other children his age. Frankly, I was probably lucky I didn't get a punch in the face from any of the other mums for being so proud. Well, it wasn't my fault I had given birth to a wunderkind. Jealousy is a very unattractive quality in a person I said to myself in a rather superior manner. Mind you, it was just as well Tom was bright as he would be the youngest in his class when he started primary school.

The remainder of Tom's pre-school years passed in a rather monotonous blur of routine, with nothing especially remarkable taking place in our lives. It was actually quite a lonely time, and I knew something had to change if I was to feel happy again.

24

School daze

Today was the first day of the rest of my life. *What a bloody silly expression*, I thought to myself. Surely every day is the first day of the rest of a person's life, isn't it? I made a mental note to Google its origins, just as soon as I had packed Tom off to school. Yes, mummy's little angel was starting full-time school. Hurrah!

After four years, at the grand old age of very-nearly-forty-two, I was finally getting my life back. Well, between the hours of nine and three at least. Actually make that 9:15 a.m. and 2:30 p.m. to allow for travelling and parking. But still, all that lovely time to myself. Much as I loved Tom, being a mother hadn't quite filled whatever hole it was that I was trying to fill. I still had no idea what was missing; I still felt like a jigsaw puzzle with bits missing. Husband, puppy, baby: pieces had all slotted into the overall picture, but crucial edge pieces were still missing along with a big bit in the middle. The jigsaw box was picture-less and gave me no clues as to what those pieces looked like. Still, I couldn't wait to have 'me time' again. I thought of all the books I hadn't had time to read, the mind-numbing daytime television I could watch to my heart's content. No-one to please but myself. Bliss!

Before I could start the rest of my life each day, I would have to face the daily battle of getting Tom washed, dressed, fed and ready for school. I was to discover that this was no mean feat and that morning stress levels would often peak at around 8:25 a.m. with me screaming at Tom to get his shoes on. 'Now! Or we're going to be late.' *How on earth did parents with more than one child ever get out of the house in the morning in any semblance of order?* I wondered. It was all I could do to get one small person and myself to an approximate state of readiness and out the door on time.

Thank goodness I was too lazy to worry about hair and make-up. My face got a dollop of moisturiser and my hair got brushed. If it was too awful it got fixed back. I think the expression for a woman like me is 'slummy mummy'. I assumed that the 'yummy mummies' got up a great deal earlier than me to make themselves look so immaculate. I bet they didn't eat chocolate chip brioches in bed with their children while watching *Peppa Pig* in the morning either. If they ate breakfast at all it was probably a wheatgrass smoothie with added aloe vera and antioxidants, which they would enjoy after their detoxifying glass of hot water with lemon juice. Just the thought of the withdrawal headache I'd get should I ever detox had me reaching for the coffee.

Secretly though, I wanted to be more like these beautiful women, with their size ten figures, perfectly cut and coloured hair, flawless make-up and golden tans. *Where did they get the self-discipline from?* I wondered. I was convinced that I must be missing out on some vital girly gene: the footballers' wives' gene as I came to think of it. I liked to look nice if I was going out somewhere special, but those times were few and far between since becoming a parent. But I really couldn't be bothered with make-up on a daily basis. I kind of liked the fact that when I *did* make the effort the impact was much greater. Admittedly it could scare small children if they were seeing the made-up me for the first time, but I could never be the kind of woman who wouldn't leave the house without her 'face' on. The pressure to always look perfect must be immense, I told myself. Think of the added stress to your daily life. I wasn't lazy, I was just sensible.

I wondered if the husbands of these perfect creatures ever saw them in their natural state. What a bizarre idea to have to conceal yourself behind a mask of cosmetic products. Maybe these women weren't quite so perfect after all. Maybe they had their own insecurities and their concealer was hiding more than just dark circles. My reasoning was working and I no longer wanted to be more like these poor sad women. They deserved my pity, not my envy. Excellent, Lucy, you're not such a lazy cow after all. You're simply secure in your own skin and confident in the way you look. Hurrah! Thank God I'm easily swayed or I may have become quite despondent as I stood in the playground surrounded by WAGs worthy of, if not the Premier League, at least Division One.

Now, I'm not saying I'm fickle or anything, but I'd be useless on a debating team: I would switch sides with each new argument raised and end up not knowing what the hell I'd believed in the first place. I'm an advertiser's dream too and am always buying the latest 'wonder cleaner' in the belief that it will revolutionise my life as a housewife. And although I tell myself that if something sounds too good to be true then it probably is, there's always a little part of me that wants to believe.

So, some mornings I still found myself looking enviously at the yummier mummies, mentally noting that their clothes most definitely did not come from a well-known supermarket chain. Unlike mine. And I envied their ability to wear high heels all day without the aid of vodka, while my feet were shoved into flat boots or trainers. Not even trendy trainers at that. But in the blink of an eye, I could convince myself of the untold damage they were doing to their feet and the back problems they were storing up for later life. Silly, vain things, I thought. You shouldn't have to suffer to look good. And I liked my flat boots. Really I did. Besides, anything else would have looked silly with my jeans and sweatshirt…

Thankfully, Tom took to school like a duck to water. Shame he hadn't taken to water like a duck, I mused, remembering a recent trip to the swimming pool, as I filled his water bottle ready for another day of 'learning through play'. I was relieved and pleased when he went off to class happily each morning as it meant I didn't have to spend all day worrying about him. That would seriously have upset my 'me time' and probably resulted in even more comfort eating than usual. On this particular day, however, I was a mum on a mission.

25

Mummy's little angel

It was early December and the school's nativity play was in rehearsal. I had to make four-year-old Tom an angel costume. When I first learned he'd been cast as an angel I'd had to fight back the laughter. How could his teacher have failed to hear the irony in my voice when I called him 'mummy's little angel'? I'd seen a multitude of angel costumes in the shops, but they were all far too girly and more like fairy costumes if you asked me. Not wanting Tom to feel any more uncomfortable about being an angel than he already did, I vowed to be a proper mummy for once and make him a costume which wouldn't make him look like a girl.

I didn't want to spend a small fortune on something which would probably only be worn once (I really couldn't see Tom ever feeling the need to go to a friend's fancy dress birthday party as one of God's winged messengers) so I took myself off to the local pound shop in search of a cheap white sheet. I bought a king size one to allow for multiple mistakes and set off home to create Tom a celestial costume he would be proud to wear. Or at least wouldn't refuse to put on altogether.

The sheet, being of less than ideal quality, was a bit on the thin side. Actually you could see right through it. No matter, I thought, as Tom would have his school uniform on underneath. So, I set to work, cutting and sewing (well, alright,

'Wundawebbing') and attaching gold tinsel round the sleeves and neck for a bit of heavenly bling. I drew the line at a halo though: I could just imagine it slipping halfway through the performance. When I'd finished I was quite pleased with myself. OK, so I wouldn't be showing at London Fashion Week anytime soon, but Tom wouldn't look like Tinkerbell and I could sit proudly in the audience with all the other proper mummies. Blimey, next thing you know I'd be baking cakes, making home-made jam, reading Woman's Weekly and darning socks.

The day of the nativity play arrived and I kissed Tom goodbye as he skipped happily into school. I say skipped, but he hadn't quite got the hang of skipping yet, so it was more of a hop, step, hop, step, action. Boys and skipping eh? They're just wrong together anyway. I wasn't even going to think about the prospect of May Day celebrations before I had to. The play wasn't until after lunch and I hoped that Tom would manage to get more of his lunch in his mouth than around it. He was still a really messy eater and often came home with more of his yoghurt on his sweatshirt than must be in his stomach. Combined with the fact that he had a bit of a cold at the moment and was inclined to wipe his nose with the back of his hand, spreading snot across his cheeks, Tom had the potential to be a rather grubby little angel. I consoled myself with the thought that at least his costume would be perfect.

I managed to get a seat in the front row and on the side of the angels, and waited with all the other proud parents for our little darlings to troop in. I saw Tom's angelic face and halo of fair hair as the line of four and five-year-olds approached the stage, and felt a surge of pure love and motherly pride. My beautiful boy. And his beautiful red pants. Oh bum. They hadn't put his costume over his school uniform, and Tom's bright red Power Ranger pants shone like a beacon through the cheap white sheet. Oh well, at least the shepherds and wise men would have no trouble locating the stable if the star of Bethlehem disappeared behind a cloud.

Thankfully, everyone was either too busy watching their own little cherubs, or were too polite to let on that they'd seen Tom's pants, and soon his lower half was concealed behind a row of stars and sheep. My relief was short-lived when the angels took centre stage a few minutes later, but at least from the front his gold tinsel belt hid some of the problem. No amount of strategically placed tinsel could have concealed Tom's actions however. He decided that it would be a good idea to wink and do a thumbs-up at every opportunity. *That's my boy,* I laughed and I resolved to buy him a cheeky monkey costume for future use.

26

School for mums

In an attempt to make life as easy as possible for myself on school days, I had arranged for Tom to have school dinners. That way I didn't have to flap about making a packed lunch every morning and he wouldn't need a cooked meal in the evening. Me lazy? I resemble that remark. As with so many of the best laid plans of mice and mums, this was not to be.

'Mummy, I really can't have school dinners anymore,' Tom grumbled after school one day. 'All my friends have packed lunches, with stuff they actually like in. I don't like being different. And, anyway, school dinners are yuck. Even worse than granny's cooking.'

'I'm sure none of your friends think anything of it, Tom,' I countered. I wasn't giving in without a fight.

'They do. They laugh and point and pretend to try and guess what the food even is.' Tom stuck his bottom lip to emphasise the awfulness of his predicament.

'It can't be that bad. I used to love school dinners.'

'But that was in the olden days, mummy.'

'When dinosaurs roamed the earth,' I couldn't help laughing.

'That's another thing, 'coz I have cooked lunch at school, you never cook me turkey dinosaurs for tea.' Damn! Why did I have to mention dinosaurs? This kid never missed a trick.

I knew that my stubborn little boy wasn't going to budge,

and this particular battle really wasn't important enough to pursue, so I relented and promised to make him a pack-up every day. I tried to look on the bright side – at least I'd know what he'd eaten and it would save money. Sometimes, if I was feeling particularly organised, I even made his sandwiches the night before. To be truthful, this was less about being organised and more about an extra five minutes in bed in the morning.

The main problem with Tom's lunchbox was what happened to all the leftovers. In the bottom of the bag would be a disgusting mess of banana, yoghurt, chocolate milk and other no longer identifiable bits of leftover food. It wouldn't have been so bad if I could've just tipped it all straight into the bin, but I had to retrieve the teaspoon he'd used for his yoghurt. In fact, it was such a revolting experience, I thought about suggesting a new bush tucker trial to the makers of *I'm a Celebrity Get Me Out of Here* which involved the contestants putting their hands inside one of Tom's finished lunch bags in an attempt to remove the missing spoon. They'd soon be begging to eat kangaroo's bits.

School was not only a learning experience for Tom. I found myself facing all sorts of challenges too. How to remove paint and pen marks from white polo shirts was a particularly useful one. I still couldn't quite work out how Tom could get orange paint on his back though. Either he was a contortionist who forgot to put his brush down before scratching that annoying itch on his back, or someone had mistaken his t-shirt for a sheet of paper. (Well, I did get those shirts *really* white.) Then there were the black pen marks which no amount of stain removal product could shift. The other mums found these equally tricky, so I didn't feel too much of a failure. We regularly moaned about the fact that our children should only have access to washable ink, and the really brave mums did have words with the teacher. Needless to say, I was not one of those.

Not only did I graduate in the fine art of stain removal, I also considered myself a trained nit nurse. We regularly received letters about the problem of head lice, asking that we checked our children's hair frequently and took any necessary action. It made my head itch just thinking about it and I vowed to lie if I ever found any of the disgusting little critters on Tom's head. We were given detailed instructions on wet-combing their hair, so I bought a nit comb (from a chemist in another town just in case anyone saw me) and psyched myself up to check Tom's hair in the bath that night. It was a huge relief when I didn't find any eggs or creepy crawlies, but I still lived in fear of the day when I wasn't so lucky. Should that day ever come, then Tom would be going to school with impenetrable amounts of wax and spray in his hair. That should stop the little blighters. Thank goodness he wasn't a girl – all that long hair and hugging. Yeuch!

Nits were another hot topic of conversation for us mums while we waited for our kids to come out at three o'clock. We bemoaned the fact that the nit nurse was no longer as frequent a visitor to school as the nits themselves.

'When we were girls,' we'd say, 'Nitty Nora the flea explorer used to come and check everyone's hair.'

Whatever happened to the nit nurses we wondered? And why would anyone want to be one in the first place? We all agreed that it wouldn't have been our career of choice. Then we all scratched our heads some more. We knew it was stupid to consider nits dirty, but there remained a stigma attached to people who had them. We'd all been told that nits prefer clean hair too, but this made no difference as we bitched about the itchy head brigade on the other side of the playground.

Cliques are inevitable. This was another lesson learned at school. Before Tom started school, I always knew I was a bit on the snobby side, but I thought I would get to know my fellow parents before making my mind up about them. But, as the saying goes, first impressions last, and some of my first impressions have certainly had staying power. To say I was relieved that Tom hadn't befriended certain children would be an understatement of gargantuan proportions. There's an inevitability about both parents and children of similar backgrounds and ideologies being drawn together. Yes, snobbery was alive and well and living in me. I couldn't help it.

I did, however, have to rethink some of my first impressions, and mums I had concluded were stand-offish or snobby (perish the thought) proved to be really lovely people and subsequently became good friends. It is of course pure coincidence that these ladies were not of the itchy head brigade.

Thinking about first impressions made me wonder what the other mums initially thought about me. What a terrifying thought. (For them as well as me probably.) How had I come across to them? Bearing in mind that my enormous boobs arrived in the school playground some time before the rest of me, they probably thought I'd come across rather too easily, and took care to keep their husbands away from me.

Thank goodness the mums that mattered were able to look past my chest (as long as I didn't turn sideways) and get to know me better before writing me off as some over-inflated tart who'd entice their husbands away, like a siren luring sailors onto the rocks, I'd lure them onto my boulders. I soon made it clear to them that my boobs were the bane of my life; the cause of no end of physical pain in my neck, shoulders and back. Not to mention the nightmare of finding bras and clothes to fit. One way or another, the boobs had to go. And preferably before the next sports day.

27

Pole dancing and tassels

'You need this operation.'

As the consultant plastic surgeon uttered these potentially life-changing words, she was hefting my ample bosom out of the way to measure around my rib cage. (Said bosom had now been subjected to forty-two years of gravity and was looking less than perky.) My level of embarrassment increased as I started to panic about what she might find under there: long lost toys, a basket of dirty washing, a small village… She might never see her tape measure again.

After the humiliation was over and I had heaved my bosom back into place, I heaved a sigh of relief. To finally be told that I wasn't mad (well, she had only just met me and would have time to reconsider at a later date) and that a breast reduction would drastically improve my quality of life was like a great weight had been lifted from my shoulders. I couldn't wait for the literal weight to be lifted too.

I handed over a hundred pounds to pay for the private consultation and headed for the car park with a mixture of elation and dread. I was so thrilled finally to see some light at the end of the tunnel, and hoped that I might even one day soon get to see the feet at the end of my legs. But mixed with this elation was an almost crippling fear of the operation itself. As I started the car and began the drive home, some of the surgeon's words had come to mind. Dog ears. (I hadn't liked to ask what exactly dog ears were, but had visions of droopy breasts like spaniel ears.) Nipple necrosis. (Didn't this basically mean dead?) Grafts. Revision surgery. (Apparently, owing to the vast distances my nipples would have to move, I may need more than one operation. I assumed this did not mean they would reduce one breast at a later date. That really would be a talking point.) Ooh it all sounded so delightful. Then I thought of the pain I was in on a daily basis and knew that these were risks I had to take. It didn't stop me remembering the photographs of what could go wrong though. I tried to put the words and images out of my head and continued on my way home. Thankfully, the car knew the route to take.

Lying in bed that night (not on my front – that just wasn't possible) I thought about my initial foray into the world of breast reduction surgery. I had asked my GP to refer me on the NHS, only to be told that my Body Mass Index was too high (i.e. I was too fat) and that I would not be accepted unless I lost weight. It was apparent that only I could see the irony of the fact that my BMI would drop nicely if they reduced the size of my now 32K bust. I went home deflated on that occasion. More wishful thinking.

So then I started thinking about going private. But how on earth was I going to find six thousand pounds? I considered glamour modelling. For about a nano-second. I wasn't that desperate yet. Besides, I didn't think the magazines would be interested in a middle-aged housewife with a bag over her head. Get a grip woman. How about selling a kidney? Far too chicken for that. Do chickens even have kidneys? This was getting me nowhere. Fast.

My friends were as helpful as ever when we got together at the soft play centre after school the next day. Once all the kids had disappeared into the ball pit or headed off to one of the slides and our much needed lattes were purchased, we relaxed back into our seats. I had just taken a sip of coffee when Charlie piped up: 'How about a fundraiser? I can just imagine the posters!' I laughed along with the girls and soon we were all coming up with ideas for the fundraiser.

'Guess the names and weights of the boobs,' Sarah suggested.

'That would get the blokes putting their hands in their pockets,' Charlie giggled.

I'd been taking a sip of coffee at that point, and nearly choked on the hot liquid.

'What?!' said Charlie, all innocence. 'I meant, for loose change, to have a go.'

'Of course you did,' I laughed, wiping coffee from my chin.

Then Zoe came up with ideas from the more traditional fair: hoopla and darts. I winced until she explained that we'd be using balloons. Not to be outdone, Claire then threw 'pin the tail onto the donkey' into the mix. The rest of us looked bemused until she explained that this was simply the idea behind 'pin the tassels on the nipples'. As our laughter grew ever more raucous it crossed my mind that we were in danger of being the first mums to be thrown out of PJ's Funhouse. Did that stop us? Don't be daft.

'We'll need prizes,' Zoe continued.

'How about soft toys for the winners? Puppies, naturally. And it goes without saying that the losers should get booby prizes,' Sarah said.

'We'd need refreshments too. What about a beer tent?' said

Charlie. 'We could use one of your bras Lucy. It'd save a fortune on hiring a marquee. We could serve pints of Guinness in one cup – with boob imprints instead of shamrocks, and cocktails in the other side. Slippery Nipples come to mind for starters.'

'Now you're being ridiculous.' I responded. 'My bras are big but they're not *that* big. You could probably get a few swing boats out of them though.'

'Wouldn't have to hire a bouncy castle, either, Luce.' Zoe made her point by giving her own boobs a quick bounce. I nearly choked on my coffee again.

In spite of the brilliance of our money-making scheme, I wasn't convinced the PTA would agree for this to take place at the primary school's summer fete. Thank God I could still laugh about it because the constant pain in my back and shoulders was just that. A real pain.

I so wanted to be able to reach to paint my own toe nails rather than relying on Paul. Or worse, Tom. Then it was more toe painting than nails. I wanted to be able to read in the bath without hoisting my boobs out of the way every time I needed to turn the page. I wanted to wear tops with buttons down the front. I think the last time I wore anything with buttons that didn't gape was at school. Best days of my life, I sighed.

I think Tom must have had some sort of sixth sense to my state of mind as he chose this moment to do a spot of pole dancing. There were several metal poles covered in padding supporting various parts of the soft play area and when we looked round Tom was hanging off one of them.

'Look, mum, I'm pole dancing.'

Everyone screamed with laughter at the sight of my son wrapping himself around the pole and shaking his behind.

After my initial shock at what he was doing, I asked Tom where on earth he had learnt about pole dancing.

'Grandad showed me,' came his proud reply.

'Are you sure he didn't mean a Maypole?' I questioned.

But I knew perfectly well Grandad John hadn't meant an innocent skip around the Maypole. I could just imagine the twinkle in his eye as he initiated his young grandson in the art of exotic dancing.

'Wait 'til I catch up with your Grandad!'

Of course all my friends, not to mention all the other parents present at the funhouse, thought it was hilarious and are convinced I have a pole hidden away at home for private use. In Paul's dreams. Mind you, it is supposed to be really good exercise...

28

Pudding rules

It looked as though the only thing I could do was lose weight and have the op on the good old NHS. As a compulsive comfort eater I really didn't think I had the will power to diet. I certainly wouldn't be able to resist my PMS chocolate cravings. My thin friends said it would be a piece of cake. Ha bloody ha. The only cakes I could see on my horizon were rice cakes. And I was convinced that they were the result of a mix up in a polystyrene tile factory. They said just don't buy any fattening foods. OK, I said, but what about Tom's chocolate buttons that I stole on a regular basis? We were talking about a woman who had been known to eat other people's Easter eggs and have to replace them before the Easter bunny found out. Feeling hopeless I munched on a bar of Dairy Milk, took a couple of painkillers and vegged out on the sofa to watch *Loose Women*.

It was soon after this that I hit rock bottom. Hard. Despite the padding. I rang my sister for sympathy and was pretty much told to sort myself out. Not the shoulder to cry on I was hoping for, but maybe the kick up the backside I needed. Next stop Weight Watchers.

While the foot imprint was still fresh on my behind I found out when and where the nearest Weight Watchers meeting was and persuaded my sister, Katie, to come with me. She didn't take much persuading as she had her own spare tyre to deflate.

Katie was the middle sister, three years older than me and eight inches shorter. As a result of her height, or lack thereof, any extra weight was harder to carry than it was for me. We didn't really look alike, but somehow people always knew we were sisters. Katie was the quiet one of us and liked to be invisible. With her shoulder-length brown hair and glasses, I had never known Katie to wear make-up. She never did anything that might draw attention to her.

So, the following Thursday evening saw us girding our loins (perhaps that should be girdling) in preparation for the dreaded weigh in.

While we were queuing up to step on to the scales I took the opportunity to remove my watch, empty my pockets and take out my hair slide.

'What are you doing?' Katie sounded bemused.

'Every little helps,' I whispered back. 'I think maybe next time I'll go commando and leave my bra at home too.' Well, the amount of wire and fabric involved in making one of my bras was not inconsiderable.

'I don't think that's a good idea,' Katie snorted. I think she could foresee a nasty tripping accident.

'You're probably right,' I sighed. 'Besides, didn't mum tell us always to wear clean undies in case we got run over and taken to hospital?' I remember thinking at the time that if I got run over, the last thing on my mind would be whether or not I had clean undies on. Still, these pearls of wisdom from your mum tend to stay with you. I never could wear an ankle chain after she said only a certain type of woman wore them. If you get my drift. Imagine how mortified I was when my very first boyfriend bought me one...

Anyhoo, as we neared the scales I started to feel a little nauseous. Might be another couple of ounces, I thought. But then the awful moment was upon me and I stepped on to the scales whilst muttering about big bones and my boobs weighing a ton. Several in fact. But the lady on the numbers end of the scales didn't bat an eyelid and the scales didn't creak and groan. (That must have been me then.) Relieved that at least part of the ordeal was over Katie and I took our seats at the front of the hall for the meeting itself. It would have been a great place for people watching if I hadn't been so preoccupied with breathing in and looking slim. I couldn't help but notice one lady though, with a floral tent-like dress and a hair-do reminiscent of a certain prominent MP in the Conservative party. I later learned that she'd lost nearly eighty pounds.

The group leader approached the stage; a really slim blonde woman. It was hard to believe she'd ever had a weight problem, but apparently the enormous pair of jeans she held up had once been worn by her. I refrained from asking who else was in them with her at the time. Her name was Eleanor Twig (I know, right!) and she explained that from now on we must make a note of everything we ate and drank and record how many 'points' we consumed each day. We each received a booklet in which to record these details. I thought I might need extra pages but, not wanting to draw attention to myself, I resolved to write really small.

Before leaving the meeting I stocked up on sweets, toffee bars and cakes from the sales table. They weren't cheap and, from what I could make out, they just took out the fat and replaced it with sugar, but I was going to need substitutes for my usual snacks. The following day I also went to the supermarket to check out what else was available to those of us counting points. Imagine my delight when I discovered Weight Watchers carrot cakes! My absolute favourite cake in the whole world. Each cake was worth two points and my daily allowance was twenty-two points. That meant I could have eleven carrot cakes a day! Yippee! Obviously I couldn't eat anything else except vegetables, and drink only black tea and coffee or water but what the heck. When PMS struck I'd be ready for it!

Well, all I can say is that when it comes to losing weight, public humiliation is the way to go. With the prospect of next week's weigh-in weighing heavy on my mind, I found it relatively easy to cut down the amount of junk I was eating. No more chocolate chip brioches in bed in the morning for me. Now it was a bowl of 'Special K'. (Special 32K in my case.) I would just enjoy inhaling as I opened the brioche bag for Tom. And maybe just sneak a tiny nibble or two before I handed them to him. Clearly Tom was going to have to develop a taste for low-fat breakfast cereal.

That said, I persevered with the diet and limited myself to one carrot cake a day. And one rich toffee bar. And some fruit sweets. And a carrot cake. I knew the diet was working though - my jeans were definitely getting a bit baggier. Despite this, I was still overcome with the same feeling of nausea the next time I queued up at the scales. Imagine my relief when I was told I'd lost four pounds. Even though I was still wearing all my underwear. Woo hoo! Katie had done even better, losing four and a half pounds. I bet *she* had left her Bridget Jones's at home. Leaving the meeting with fresh hope, we resisted the urge for a celebratory fish and chip supper and went home to continue our good work. Little did I know the trouble that lay ahead. In the shape of a pineapple upside-down cake.

Paul was loosely following the Weight Watchers plan with me. He really wanted to help and knew I needed all the support I could get. In so many ways. But he was an evening-snacker like me and dieting made him pretty miserable. As if he wasn't miserable enough with enforced near-celibacy. What a fun-filled few weeks we were in for! I suggested to Tom that he might like to move in with Granny for a while. Either that or spend his pocket money on a flak jacket. He looked at me with a rather puzzled expression. Sometimes I forgot he was only five. I gave him a hug, told him how much I loved him and vowed to threaten Paul with unutterable torture if he took his misery out on Tom.

It was during the second week of the diet that Paul broke. We'd had a ridiculously healthy dinner of steamed salmon and vegetables and I was feeling extremely virtuous. Yes, I had a horrendous craving for something sweet but I would content myself with a 'thick and creamy' Weight Watchers' yoghurt for only half a point. (I think I could have sued them under the Trades Description Act for the 'thick and creamy' reference.) Paul, however, had other ideas and sloped off to the kitchen where he proceeded to concoct a pineapple and golden syrup sponge pudding. It was a variation on pineapple upside down pudding. The variation being that it wasn't upside down.

I could smell the sponge as it cooked and I knew that resistance was going to be futile. Sure enough, when the pudding was cooked, I gave in and ate a small serving as slowly as I could, savouring every mouthful. God it was good. I knew this was only the start of my ordeal as the guilt kicked in. There was still half the pudding left after Paul had tucked in. I wasn't going to be safe until the whole thing had been consumed. I think I probably dreamed of hot, sweet sponge pudding that night and I awoke knowing that it was waiting downstairs to tempt me some more. Oh God, how I wanted it!

I managed to keep myself busy all morning and stuck rigidly to my diet. But I could hear the delicious dessert calling to me with its syrupy smoothness. Get a grip woman, I told myself. Think of why you're on this sodding diet in the first place. To get that much needed breast reduction. But it was no good and I found myself guiltily spooning a few small mouthfuls of sponge straight from the serving bowl. Hopefully Paul wouldn't even notice. He wasn't the most observant of men normally, but this was pudding and normal rules did not apply.

That night we polished off the remaining pudding between us and I was relieved that it was no longer able to seduce me in a moment of weakness. Especially since my moments of weakness tended to last for several hours at a time. But of course I was riddled with guilt and panic-stricken at the thought of my next weigh-in. I'd done so well in the first week, and now I'd fallen at the second fence, nobbled by my own husband. If he tried such dirty tactics again I would see to it that there was no other 'nobb' related activity for a very long time.

It also occurred to me that he might be trying to sabotage my weight-loss plan deliberately. I knew Paul loved me the way I was and was scared at the prospect of me changing. I think he was also quite proud to have a wife who could out-do Jordan on the boob front. But he wasn't the one turning into Quasimodo. And perish the thought if I ever had to run for a bus. I'd be wearing sunglasses to hide the black eyes for weeks. I'm not saying I was being blasé about the operation. Far from it. I was absolutely terrified at the prospect of having some stranger taking a scalpel to my breasts. These were the same breasts that had fed my beautiful baby boy, and they were brilliant for hiding extra bellies under. But having the reduction was a risk I had to take. The alternative was a life of pain and increasing back problems which greatly reduced the quality of my life already.

The week continued to conspire against me as I battled against pre-menstrual cravings. Normally I gave in to these cravings and scoffed everything in sight. Except salad, fruit or anything vaguely healthy. Somehow I just never craved lettuce. And don't try telling me that a chocolate orange isn't one of my five-a-day when I've got PMS. You may not live to regret it. Combine this with water retention and constipation caused by my pain killers and I was feeling like a lost cause. The public humiliation loomed large on the horizon that was Thursday.

I faced trial by scales with my usual mix of nausea and humour and was relieved that by some minor miracle I had lost one-and-a-half pounds. Hallelujah! There is a God! And he is good. And he approves of pineapple right-way-up pudding. The relief was immense. It couldn't all be down to the fact that I'd had more than my usual trim at the hairdressers and my nails were the shortest they'd been for years. (I'd even removed my toe nail polish.) I must still be doing something right. Katie continued to do better than me by losing two pounds, but I wasn't surprised as she had more than my miniscule amount of willpower and was not such a greedy cow as me. We were both delighted at being close to losing our first half a stone. But could we keep it up? Only time would tell. And those bloody scales of course.

And so commenced another week of battling my food demons and eating my own body weight in steamed vegetables. I began to fantasise about fish and chips, burgers with the works, fresh cream cakes and deep fried Mars bars. (I'd never tried one of these but I was quite sure they were amazing.) Move over Danny Campbell, there's no room for you in my bed with all this lovely grub...

29

St. Paul of kitchen

I'd arranged another after school play date for the kids the following Monday and we all met up at PJs. We established ourselves at our usual table, waved off the children and settled down for a catch up. It was the usual suspects: me, Zoe, Charlie, Sarah and Claire. Zoe had recently had baby number two and we all took turns to have a cuddle. I would've preferred a puppy but bravely offered to hold baby Olivia while Zoe went to get a jug of squash. I had never been much of a fan of tiny babies but Olivia was sweet and had just started to smile. I hoped Tom wouldn't get any ideas about having a baby brother or sister if he saw me with babe in arms, because he'd be disappointed. Aside from the fact that I was over forty and felt too old and tired to do the whole sleepless night thing again, his dad had gone for the snip about a year earlier.

Any tiny lingering doubt about wanting to be a mum again was soon quashed when the conversation turned to childbirth. Whenever a group of women get together (well this group anyway) certain topics inevitably seem to arise. Sex, childbirth/children and men. Oh, and women's problems. Of which, naturally, the aforementioned sex, men and children are the prime examples.

After we had compared parturition horror stories (why, oh, why did any woman ever go on to have a second baby?) the conversation turned to husbands. And partners for those of the group who'd had the good sense not to get married. Poor Zoe was bemoaning the fact that her partner Steve did absolutely nothing to help with either the children or the house.

'He's never bathed them or put them to bed, and the one and only time I asked him to put the oven on while I did the school run, I had to leave him with a diagram of the cooker knobs and written instructions.' She sighed.

I thought about Paul, who usually did the bedtime routine and was a really hands-on dad. Admittedly he didn't notice things that needed doing in the house unless they were pointed out to him, but I guess that's a man thing. They just see things differently. That goes double for what they see in the mirror. When a woman looks in the mirror she sees all the things she doesn't like about her body, a whole host of imperfections – imagined or otherwise. But when a man looks in the mirror he is magically transformed into a veritable God. Paul has been known to admire himself naked in the mirror and then turn to me with the words 'God, you're lucky.' Apparently, 'Why's that then?' was not the response he was hoping for.

Men would be so much better if they were only more like women. The more I think about the differences between the sexes, the more I think my friend Ali has got the right idea. She left her husband for another woman and has never been happier. I've only met her partner, Louise, once, but it was clear they were made for each other. Louise was a pretty, petite contrast to Ali, with a fragile beauty that suggested a kind and gentle nature. There was a relaxed affection between them that I'd never seen with Ali and her husband. Ali and Louise just looked right together and Ali, despite her masculine looks and ways, glowed like a woman in love. It was a joy to see my friend looking so happy, so complete. I wondered if I was ever going to find the sort of deep contentment that these two had found.

I do believe that men and women are, on the whole, incompatible. When the honeymoon period is over and sex has become not so much a thrill as a chore, we see men in a different light. Off preferably. The little foibles which were once tolerated with an understanding smile now drive us to distraction. Instead of wanting to bring them a delicious and lovingly prepared full English in bed, we now want to hit them over the head with the frying pan in which we used to cook it. No more whispering sweet nothings in his ear. Now it's screaming like a fishwife for him to put the bloody toilet lid down.

I then regaled the girls with a few of Paul's annoying habits. Like never closing drawers, and never putting anything away when he's finished with it. Then he moans because he can't find anything, goes out and buys a new one just in time to find the old one.

'Then there was the time I put some leftover sausages in the fridge in a bowl. He took the sausages out and left the empty bowl in the fridge. A woman would never have done that.'

I confessed to calling Paul Mister-Half-a-Job because he never finished anything. Then I felt a pang of guilt as I thought of all the things he did help me with. Instead of focussing on what he didn't do, I really should give him more credit for the things (or half things) that he did do.

It was somehow comforting to listen to other women's tales about their other halves. It made you realise that a) maybe you should count your blessings and b) they all had their little, or not so little, annoying habits. I often vowed to go home and be nicer to Paul after one of these sessions. Unfortunately for Paul, by the time I got home something would inevitably have happened to push this resolution firmly to the back of mind. These days it was usually how bloody hungry I was.

When we'd put the world temporarily to rights, we rounded up our offspring, said our goodbyes and set off home. I still had to come up with something tasty and low fat for dinner. Previously I would have called in at the chippy on the way for two large cod and chips or nipped to the drive-through for burgers, fries and cokes. With a sigh, I forced myself to drive straight past those dens of gluttonous iniquity and was soon pulling onto our drive.

As I entered the house, dropping Tom's book bag, lunch box and water bottle on the hall table as I went, I could smell something delicious coming from the kitchen. Yes, you guessed it, Paul, my saint of a husband, had made a healthy, low calorie dinner. And not a pineapple right-way-up pudding in sight.

30

Death by pizza

It was 8:20 a.m. and I was doing my usual frantic pre-school preparations. Not for the first time I thanked my lucky stars I'd had a boy and most days I could get away with not bothering to brush his hair. Occasionally if Tom had a bad case of bed hair I just wet it a bit and smoothed it down as we were going out the door. I could only imagine the nightmare faced every morning by mothers of girls with long hair. All that untangling and brushing, not to mention pony tails, bunches, plaits and an endless supply of scrunchies and hair clips to be kept track of. If I'd had a daughter she'd have had to be a Tom boy. Ha ha! Anyway, it was five minutes 'til the 'shoes on' shout and the bloody phone rang.

Paul arrived at work at 8 a.m. each day and had decided that it would be a good idea to phone home at about 8:20 a.m. each morning to make sure we're up. If we weren't, I thought to myself, it was a bit bloody late now. Usually his phone call was timed to coincide with teeth brushing which was never an enjoyable part of the morning routine. Come to think of it, now the chocolate chip brioches had gone from my diet, there was nothing pleasurable about the morning routine. Cleaning the teeth of a reluctant five-year-old who doesn't want to miss *Lazy Town* required the patience of a saint. A saint I ain't, as I yelled at Tom to open his mouth so I could see his teeth. This was the point at which I reminded myself he still hadn't been to a dentist yet, and I vowed to remedy that at the earliest opportunity. Just as soon as I could find an NHS dentist with places available. That'd be never then.

I always answered the phone when it rang. For one thing Paul would worry if I didn't. And for another it could be one of the other mums needing help. Or it could be an emergency. Although those type of calls usually come in the middle of the night don't they? Why is that? Anyway, I answered the phone and Paul said:

'You sound breathless. Are you OK?'

'I was in the middle of cleaning Tom's teeth and had to drop everything to rush to the phone, in case it was an emergency,' hoping that he'll take the hint that this really isn't the best time to call. But let's face it, men just don't get subtle. I didn't want to have a go at him about phoning because he meant well, but… aaaaaggggggghhhhhhhh! A woman would have realized it wasn't a good time to ring. I would just have to explain to him in the nicest way I could, using words of one syllable, that it wasn't really convenient to come to the phone at that time of the morning. And that if he did it again I'd chop off his bits and feed them to the cats. That should get the message across, I thought.

One particular morning at around 8:20 a.m. I heard the sound of a text message arriving on my mobile. My first thought was that Paul needed to tell me something but was too scared to phone. But it wasn't Paul, it was Katie:

'I-had-a-double-chocolate-muffin-for-breakfast-and-it-wasn't-a-Weight-Watchers-one-either,' the text blurted.

'Oops!' I sent back.

'I thought it might make you feel better about the slight wobble you had this week,' replied my ever thoughtful sister.

Unfortunately, the wobbly wheels had now well and truly fallen off my diet wagon, taking me with them. I had no-one to blame but myself for this mechanical failure. I always was rubbish at maintaining anything.

I'd had to confess my sins to sister Katie and even if I had been a Catholic, no amount of Hail Marys was going to absolve me of these particular sinful acts. After I had reeled off a list of forbidden fruits which would have made Adam and Eve shudder, Katie said she'd be seriously pissed off if I had lost weight again this week. 'I might even have a strop,' she added. I said I'd probably drop down dead from the shock if I had lost weight after the serious amount of bingeing I'd done. Katie said that maybe this was a bit drastic. Neither of us would have to worry about any stropping or dropping down dead as I knew full well my next weigh in was going to be a humiliating experience. I just hoped it was humiliating enough to spur me on to do better. But right now, I had another problem. There was a tub of chocolate crispy cakes in the cupboard with my name on them. They did have Tom's name on, but I rubbed it out and wrote mine instead. Father forgive me. And son come to that.

Why did I find it so difficult not to give in to my cravings? I had the perfect incentive to lose weight for my operation, so why was I such an utter failure? I had found the first week relatively easy, but had given in to more and more temptation ever since that fateful day of the pineapple pudding. We'd gone to a Murder Mystery night at Tom's school on Friday night and I had pigged out on pizza, quiche, samosas and mini fresh cream chocolate éclairs. I tried to console myself with the knowledge that I had only drunk water all evening, appetite suppressing water at that. (According to the label.) Perhaps without it I wouldn't have stopped at three éclairs. I told myself I'd get back on track tomorrow. I seemed to be doing that a lot lately. The problem was of course that tomorrow never came.

I woke on Saturday morning with a pounding headache which further pissed me off.

'How is it that when you drink, I get the hangover?' I groaned, turning towards Paul on his side of the bed.

'I think it's more likely to be a food hangover, Luce. You did scoff an awful lot of cheese and cream last night, and they always make you feel rough.'

'Still, it's most unfair,' I mumbled. My stomach grumbled in agreement.

I was invariably the designated driver when we went out as I hadn't really started drinking again since my pregnancy. I was seriously out of practice at the drinking game and was too scared about how awful I might feel the next day to start again. Then I thought about how awful I felt and figured I might as well do something to deserve it. Other than eating my own body weight in cheese and cream. Why did things loaded with saturated fat taste so damn good? There had been a plate of crudités and a light dip on the table, but one dunk in the low fat sour cream and chive had me reaching for the delicious home-made pizza Laura had made. How was she so slim if this was the sort of thing they ate at her house? I will never know how I made myself stop at two slices. Must have been something in the water.

Does laughing burn calories I wonder? If it does then I must have burnt off a large piece of quiche that night. The other parents on our table (hand-picked by me to maximize our chances of winning the 'whodunnit' table prize) were great company. We were supposed to work out who the murderer was as we watched a small group of actors perform the mystery play. We had no excuses. Our table was closest to the stage, we had been supplied with paper and pencil to make notes and were all intelligent people. Or so I thought.

Before the play started, we had been warned to expect one gun shot at some point during the performance. I suppose they had to do this for health and safety reasons. Didn't want anyone disrupting the evening by dropping dead from a heart attack. Well, we all watched with as much concentration as a group of mostly tiddly mums and dads could muster. I had no excuse. But how hard could it be to figure out? I'd read loads of Agatha Christies over the years. We were soon pretty much convinced we knew how the murder was going to take place as there was a bottle of cough medicine in plain sight and a spilt bottle of poisonous tablets. Obviously someone was going to spike the cough medicine. The trouble was that all the characters took the bottle of cough medicine off stage at some time and all had a motive. Bugger.

During the interval we were invited to make our best guesses. In our case that should probably read absolutely useless guesses. Talk about going from one extreme to the other. We talked our way from them all being in on it – it was a conspiracy – to nobody did it: she wasn't really dead. You see we'd been thrown by the fact that there had not been a gunshot by this point in the play. It hadn't occurred to any of us that the shooting could have been anything other than the murder. So, we made our best guess and watched the concluding act. When the detective shot the guilty party as they fled the scene you could hear pennies dropping all around our table. It didn't matter in the least as everyone had had a good laugh and we'd raised some money for the school. Even if it was mostly pennies.

While the PTA was busy counting the pennies, I was busy counting calories. Oops. I may have gone slightly over my points for Friday. Never mind, it was a one-off and a special occasion. Saturday also turned into a special occasion. (I forget why. Maybe the sun was shining.) As did Sunday – well, it was Mother's Day and my mum had cooked a roast. And Monday. Monday was special because it was the day after Mother's Day. And then, on Tuesday, Paul had his annual review at work and got a good pay rise, so that was a special occasion too. We had a Chinese takeaway that night and my portion control wasn't particularly good. And the trouble with Chinese is that there are invariably leftovers. The rate I was going I would have to start squirting washing-up liquid on any uneaten food as soon as we finished eating to make damn sure it was inedible. I wasn't convinced that this would work in my case as I could see myself rinsing it off under the tap and just adding a bit of ketchup to disguise any residual lemony freshness.

Since joining Weight Watchers I had resisted weighing myself between meetings. Until now. After my text conversation with Katie about all my food sins I thought I'd just check if I'd put weight on. I needed to know whether or not to wear protective clothing when we next stepped on the scales. Katie's strops were quite something to behold and I needed to be prepared. Sure enough, when I stood on the scales in my bathroom my weight had increased by four pounds. Bugger. I had secretly been hoping that it would have stayed the same as the previous week. Slim hope, Lucy, you fat cow. Well, at least Katie wouldn't lose it with me. Mind you, somebody needed to. I was in dire need of a bloody good talking to.

With only one day left until the next meeting, I knew there was little I could do except try my best to get back on track and hope for a miracle. Or a nasty bout of food poisoning.

So, on Wednesday morning I really tried to realise my good intentions. I had a low-fat yoghurt and cereal for breakfast and a raw carrot as a snack. I had also promised myself I would go out for a bike ride. I had no more excuses now that Paul had mended the punctures in both tyres. I pulled on my trainers, tucked my trousers into my socks (mmmm, very sexy) and went out to the garage to get my bike. I tried to move it out onto the drive, but something was wrong with the front wheel. It was really stiff and I could barely get it to turn. I have to admit I didn't try terribly hard to diagnose the problem, simply pushed the thing back into the garage and decided to go for a walk instead. The thought had been there and that's what counts I told myself as I set off to power walk (that might be a slight exaggeration) around the recreation ground behind our house.

Unfortunately, my cat Marmite thought she would like to come along. Marmite was half-Siamese and she was definitely different. Now while we normally celebrated 'different' in our family, it didn't extend quite as far as taking the cat for a walk. Goats, yes, but that's a whole other story. Marmite trotted along behind me, yowling in her semi-Siamese voice. She really couldn't cope when I left the house on foot. She didn't mind if I went by car, but she hated seeing me walking away. She wasn't quite brave enough to follow me round the corner into the rec itself, so I was forced to leave her yowling in despair as I continued on my way. I decided to walk around the perimeter of the rec as fast as I could. The temptation to cut off the corners was great but I didn't cheat. Much. Well, I was worried about my beloved cat. I hurried back to where I'd left Marmite and sure enough there she was yowling away pitifully. We walked back to the house in companionable silence. Well, I did. Marmite didn't shut up until we were safely back indoors.

Later that day, with Marmite curled up on my lap, purring contentedly, I made a decision. After telling Paul that no, he couldn't stroke my pussy, I informed him that I wanted to get another cat. To keep Marmite company. Given our track record with animals I understood why he looked less than thrilled at the idea, but I soon talked him round (without having to go back on the pussy stroking thing I'm pleased to say.) After all, what could go wrong? We'd get another female kitten and the two of them would soon be the best of friends. And maybe, just maybe, another little piece of the Lucy-jigsaw would slot into place.

I soon tracked down a litter of beautiful silver tabby kittens and before Paul could change his mind, I'd told the owner we'd take one of the females. She was a gorgeous little silver fluffball and I fell in love with her instantly. (The kitten, not the owner.) We called her Lissy and she fitted right into the family and got on just fine with Marmite. Hooray.

It was when I took Lissy to the vet for her vaccination that I found out she was in fact a he. Oops. I hadn't checked when we bought her – I'd simply taken the seller at their word. (To be honest, I wouldn't really have known what I was looking at anyway.) Oh well, not a problem, we'll simply re-name him

Louie and carry on regardless. I made a mental note to get him neutered as soon as physically possible and took the little fella home.

31

Louie Le Wee

Now don't get me wrong, I really love animals. A lot. But if that sodding cat peed up my lounge curtains once more I was going to wring its scrawny neck. As I took down the curtains to wash them for the fourth time that week I was seriously pissed off with my beautiful, but oh so neurotic, cat Louie. Soon to be rechristened Le Wee if he carried on with this behaviour. He was already on a yellow card for fighting with Marmite.

Marmite was a whole other kettle of fish. What a silly saying that is. Marmite was a whole other kettle of cat isn't much better though is it? Anyway, Marmite was rather overweight due to the steroids she had to take periodically for her asthmatic condition. The vet had said that if she got any worse she'd need an inhaler. How I kept a straight face at that I don't know. Actually, I didn't. And when I had finished snorting with laughter, I was coolly informed that she'd have a mask to breathe through when I administered aforementioned inhaler. Of course that set me off again. When I eventually regained my composure the vet suggested that in the meantime Marmite could perhaps go on a diet. Well, they do say pets look like their owners. Except I couldn't blame steroids for the most attractive muffin top that protruded over the top of my jeans. As far as I knew you couldn't get salt and vinegar crisps and Mars bars on prescription. I left the vet's office suitably chastised and wondering about Weight Watchers for cats.

Anyway, where was I? Oh yes, Le Wee. With the curtains going round in the washing machine again (I was ignoring the fact that the label said Dry Clean Only) I headed back to the lounge armed with kitchen roll (where was Juan Sheet when I needed him?) and a bottle of 'Urine-Off'. I was hoping it did exactly what it said on the label, and removed every trace of cat wee. My mother-in-law had said I should rub Louie's nose in the offending patch but, as far as I could see, that would only have resulted in his nose needing a good squirt of 'Urine-Off' and probably a few scratches on me. Besides, I really loved the little sod and it wasn't his fault. He'd been badly bitten by a stray as a young cat and it had turned him into the cowardly bully he was today: terrorising his fat asthmatic housemate but too scared to go out into the garden. I couldn't blame him. There were some really big slugs out there.

Louie decided to push his luck just a little bit further the next morning. I really cannot emphasise enough how utterly disgusting the feeling of cat sick squelching between your toes is. Oh my God! I had just trudged downstairs to put the kettle on for my morning cuppa, stepped into the kitchen... and... squish. I was torn between throwing up on the spot myself, finding and strangling the offending cat, or just collapsing into a heap of 'I can't take anymore' despondency.

After a few seconds of indecisive despair, I hopped off up the stairs to take a shower to try and wash away not only the cat vomit, but the negative thoughts I was having about my beautiful boy. The little bastard. Louie decided his own fate when I pulled back the shower curtain and was met by the sight of mouse guts. I guess he didn't like offal. That was it. Louie would have to go. Right now. Well, right after I'd cleaned the shower, myself and the kitchen floor…

I rang the vet and made an appointment to take Louie in that afternoon. He yowled all the way there and I felt lousy at the thought of giving him up. He was basically a lovely cat. He just had issues. Maybe he could have counselling. Some group therapy might do the trick. So, it was with a heavy heart that I pushed open the door to the vet's and checked in at reception.

'What a beautiful cat,' the receptionist purred.

That really isn't helping, I thought, but I smiled my brightest smile at her and nodded in agreement. I couldn't bring myself to speak at this point. Waiting to go in and see the vet was like waiting to have a smear test. You know it's for your own good, but it's not going to be a particularly enjoyable experience. After just a few minutes agonised wait, the vet called out Louie's name. I would have to tell him about the new French pronunciation.

I explained Le Wee's behavioural issues to the attractive young vet. Not that I noticed he was young and attractive of course. I was much too upset.

'How close are you to re-homing him?' he asked.

'Very,' came my reply. 'In fact, if he wees in the house again my husband says he'll re-home him right into the road on the end of his boot.'

'Well, there is one last thing we can try,' said the veterinary Adonis.

'I'll try anything,' I said.

'Anti-depressants,' he said.

I was tempted to ask 'for me or the cat?' but I was too

busy wetting myself laughing. (Note to self: buy Tena Lady.) Thankfully, unlike the vet who had seen Marmite the fat asthmatic, this vet had a sense of humour. So, Louie the skinny neurotic lived to fight another day. Or not fight, with any luck. And if the anti-depressants didn't work for him, maybe I'd try taking them myself. After I'd shortened all the curtains and stocked up on 'Urine-Off'.

32

So near, so spa

My eldest sister Rose, who's four years older than me, is one of the most intelligent people I know. Not only does she have a good brain, but she uses it. After graduating from Cambridge University, Rose went on to qualify as not only an accountant, but a personnel manager and a teacher of Mathematics. Of course, I could teach maths if I wanted to. To the reception class. I scraped a B grade at 'O' level and that was to be my ultimate achievement in the area of mathematics. (How I ended up working in accounts remains a mystery, but it sure as hell has nothing to do with any mathematical talent.) I have been told that my brain is as good as Rose's. I'm just not as good at using it. Call it laziness if you want. I do. Whatever the truth, Rose is an achiever. I am a supreme under-achiever.

She's also incredibly busy. All of the time. With a large house and garden to look after, three equally busy kids and an even busier GP husband, I don't know where she finds time to teach. And tutor. And bake for cake sales. And sing in the church choir. And start up Brownies in the village. And have jewellery parties. Need I go on. Rose never stopped. It made me tired just thinking about how much she got done in a day. I think it's an achievement if do a load of washing and have something edible in the house for dinner. (Although if you spoke to Paul, he'd be only too happy to tell you how often he came home after a long day in the office and had to get his own dinner. With all that cooking, when was he going to find time to polish his halo?)

OK, so I'm no domestic goddess. The only resemblance I bear to the lovely Nigella is in the curve department. But I'd been a full-time housewife (sorry, homemaker) for six years by this time and had become something of an expert at housework avoidance. It was only the threat of visitors that made me run the vacuum cleaner round. I'd also given up ironing. Well, it was that or chocolate. I found that if I gave the washing a really good shake before I hung it up then it really wasn't too bad. Body heat took care of most creases.

Unfortunately for Paul, this rather limited his shirt options. He had to select a shirt from the few which didn't look too screwed up after washing and ignore the much larger selection which looked as though they'd been slept in. Now there's an idea: I could wear them as nightshirts. Every cloud and all that.

Having justified the lack of ironing activity, I started to think about how I could excuse the state of my car and the cobwebs around the coving… Well, the cobwebs were easy. I have always lived by the adage 'if you wish to live and thrive, let a spider run alive'. The thought of sucking the poor innocent little mites up the vacuum cleaner was unbearable, as was making them home-less. Before I knew it I'd be opening a spider refuge and a spider soup kitchen. That is a soup kitchen for spiders. Not soup made out of spiders. (I may have been born on Halloween, but I do not own a cauldron. Apart from the one I use as a planter in the garden. And I do not have jars labelled 'eye of newt' and 'spiders' legs' in my kitchen cupboard. Although I haven't cleaned out the cupboards for absolutely ages, so there may be a few undesirables lurking.) I'd just have to wait for one of the cats to catch and eat them before I demolished their dwellings. Problem solved. Survival of the fittest and all that. As for my car, I had decided to go with the hippo/elephant theory. A layer of mud would protect it from the sun. And hopefully prevent the copious amounts of pigeon poo from damaging the paint. Ingenious. I wasn't sure I'd be able to sell this idea to Paul, but as his car was equally filthy I didn't think he'd have a leg to stand on. Rather like the spiders after the cats have had a go at them.

Anyway, back to Rose. Rose was even better at housework avoidance than me. I think we were missing another vital gene needed to make up the perfect housewife. Rose had solved the problem by getting two cleaners. Actually, make that one cleaner and a tidier. She also had a gardener who helped to keep, if not on top of the huge garden, at least somewhere nearer the summit. These miracle workers allowed Rose to be even busier and cram even more into her days. And be even more exhausted. Thank God for health spas is all I can say.

Rose lived not far from the most gorgeous spa in Cambridge and was such a frequent visitor that I think she now had her own parking space and robe. Occasionally, Katie and I were lucky enough to join her for a day of complete escape and relaxation. Not to mention a fantastic opportunity to people watch and, in my case, enjoy an enormous slice of the most sublime carrot cake. (Thankfully, it was not one of those spas that allowed only a stick of celery and a glass of mineral water for lunch.)

As soon as a two-for-one offer came up at the spa we would book ourselves in. Having something like that to look forward to was a boost in itself. And the fact that Rose lived a two-hour drive away meant that we had to have at least an overnight stay.

For me this meant the added bonus of a night, or even two nights, in a bed on my own; no snoring husband and wriggly son. And I would be able to stay in the same bed all night. What luxury. At home we played musical beds most nights.

Tom invariably wandered through to our bed at some point during the night. I would often take myself off to the spare room. And it wasn't unheard of for Tom to be the only one in our bed come morning. Paul sometimes took a turn in the spare room and I would eventually crawl into Tom's bed and wrap myself exhaustedly in his Scooby Doo duvet in an attempt to get a bit more sleep before the morning rush started again. I could never understand how such a small person could take up so much of a king size bed. And Tom did have a tendency to cling on like a koala bear on a eucalyptus tree, and dig his nails in for better grip. Not a pleasant way to spend the night.

While we're on the subject, another thing that pisses me off about sleep, or the lack thereof, is my husband's ability to go straight back to it. Not only do I hear the slightest sound in the night – I think a woman develops some kind of sixth sense when she becomes a mother – but once woken I find it almost impossible to get back to sleep. I know the advice is to get up and do something before returning to bed, but I like being tucked up warm in bed and I resent having to get up and make a cup of tea or watch a bit of television until I'm sleepy once more. I don't even like putting the light on to read, even though this would probably have the desired effect. So, I lie there feeling fed up until I finally doze off just before the alarm clock sounds.

Paul, on the other hand, had been known to go downstairs to fetch Tom a drink in the night and be asleep again as soon as his head hit the pillow. The next morning, he would have no recollection of getting up at all. It's so unfair. And then he had the nerve to snore and cough and turn over at frequent intervals like some sort of large aquatic mammal, sending the mattress into what I can only liken to a tidal wave. One night, I may just smother him with his pillow. Or push him out of bed. I could blame the self-induced tsunami.

That brings me nicely back to the spa, which had installed several water beds. There was always great demand for these water beds, especially the double one on an outside balcony, which was sumptuously bedecked with furs and blankets to keep its occupants warm on even the coldest day. Naturally this attracted the couples who frequented the spa. Personally I had no desire to share my day of unadulterated bliss with my husband. I could only assume that the couples who chose to spa together were still in the honeymoon period, and thought smearing each other with mud in a private treatment room was sexy. I was quite sure that in years to come, I would see the women return with only female friends, and that the main topic of conversation would be the men they had escaped from for the day. Oh Lucy, so young and yet so cynical.

On this particular visit to the spa, couples were definitely in the majority and we found ourselves having to resist the urge to shout 'get a room' on far too many occasions. One woman in the pool had a big grin on her face and I'm quite sure that the man behind her had his foot between her legs. Oh please. Get a room! I gave them what I hoped was my dirtiest look and then pointedly turned my back on them. Only to be met by the hairiest man I had EVER seen. I'm not kidding when I say he looked as though he had got into the pool with his jumper still on. Either that or there was a new trend for hairy all-in-one swim suits. For men. I've never been a fan of hairy men but, not wanting to offend or embarrass him, I tried to wipe the look of horror off a face, which had only a moment ago been pursed with distaste. Blimey, it was like facial aerobics. I hope that I managed to contort my features into something resembling a smile and moved quickly away to one of the seated areas. (Which had a particularly enjoyable jet.)

Katie, Rose and my niece Sophie had seen my facial work-out and came over to join me, giggling like naughty school girls. When jumper-man climbed out of the pool he was wearing teeny tiny speedos. Definitely not a hairy swim-suit then. After he was out of ear shot we laughed like drains blocked with body hair and I expressed my concern that his hair may have left a sea-weedy layer across the pool, which we would have to wade through to get out. We wondered if he had an appointment for a waxing treatment while he was at the spa. They could probably remove sufficient hair to make him a hairy jumper. After all, he'd probably feel a tad chilly in only his skin.

I suppose we were being pretty bitchy about the people around us. But isn't that what groups of women do? It was harmless and I was quite sure that other people would be doing exactly the same about us. We gave them plenty of scope after all. Me with my enormous chest and Rose with her somewhat unkempt bikini line which insisted on peeping out from her swim suit. Sorry Rose, I never did tell you about that. Then there was Katie who didn't have her hearing aids in and kept missing out on vital bits of the conversation, looking confused and mumbling 'eh… what?' Only Sophie would escape people's criticism. As a slim and gorgeous 20-year-old medical student,

Sophie was just about perfect. Perfect. That would get 'em bitching with jealousy.

Being at the spa was like being in another world; completely shut off from all the drudgery of everyday life, nothing to think about except relaxing. Completely and utterly. It may sound boring, and the first time I went I took a book to pass the time. But I didn't read a single page. I just took a deep breath in. And out. (Knocking out a couple coming out of the mutual mud-smearing room with my enormous chest.) And switched off. Everything except my mouth that is. Oops. That first time at the spa I had the sort of conversation I'd never had with my sisters, before or since. I'm not sure if they were shocked or secretly impressed as I recounted some of my sex-capades while I was between husbands…

33

Between husbands

After my split from Rob, and before I met Paul, I'd been on a bit of a mission to add a few notches to my bedpost. Don't get me wrong, I didn't think I'd ever have to shout 'timber' as the bedpost fell away, but I had a few wild oats and they needed sowing.

Bizarrely, some of the best porridge was made with Rob after we'd agreed to split up. Why is it that sex is so much better when you're breaking up with someone? What's all that about? We were still the same people, with the same bodies, we just weren't going to be spending the rest of our lives together. One of the reasons we were splitting was that I would rather have had a nice cup of tea than sex, and the only thing we did in bed was read or watch TV. I understand that you have to work at this aspect of a marriage, but I really couldn't be bothered and when I did occasionally make the effort I was relieved when it was over and I could stop feeling guilty and forget about it for a while.

So how cross was I when the marriage finally ended and Rob turned into a sex god? It was amazing and heart-breaking all at the same time. Not wanting to stay married to this man, but not knowing how I could live without him. It was just so screwed up, and further proof that I was destined never to be content with my lot in life. Or, in this case, my Rob.

After Rob, things got even more bizarre.

I continued to regale my sisters with my tales of the unex-sex-ted.

'So then I joined a health club and met a fat bloke. And believe me when I tell you that you can have sensational sex with a fat bloke in the front of a sports car. As long as you don't mind the odd bruise from the gear knob, door handle etc. And foot prints on the roof. We used to drive to the beach, listening to All Saints singing (yes, you guessed it) *Pure Shores* from the movie *The Beach*. Well, after all, isn't having sex in a car a kind of rite of passage? (Admittedly, probably not when you're thirty-two, but better late than never.) I had some good times with my fat bloke (who shall remain anonymous). Lots of fast cars and exciting, risky sex.

'Then there was that time in the boardroom where he worked.'

'On the table?' Rose asked incredulously.

'Er… no… the floor,' I clarified. 'And the steam room at the Maidstone Hilton…' I continued. I think I did have the grace to blush when I regaled them with those particular episodes, but no-one would know as the room was so dimly lit.

'Weren't you worried someone would walk in on you?' Rose again.

'Of course! But that's kind of the point!' I explained.

'What would you have done if someone had come in?' Rose persisted.

'I dunno. Asked them to join in?' I giggled.

'God! Lucy! No!'

'Of course not, Rose. I don't do sharing!'

'Oh, that's alright then,' Rose said, sarcastically.

'Well, anyway, no-one did walk in on us, so we'll never know.'

'Thank God for small mercies!' Rose was clearly shocked at my antics and I knew I should really pull my head in, but my naughty streak was showing.

'Well, it may have been small, but he knew what to do with it.' I couldn't help myself.

'Jesus, Lucy. Too much information.'

I relented. 'Sorry, Rose, but after a pretty dull and empty marriage, it just felt so good to really want someone and to just live a little – really let myself go.'

Rose was quiet. I think there was a part of her that understood. And was maybe a bit jealous.

Katie had been pretty quiet throughout. I think without her hearing aids, she hadn't really kept up with the conversation. Probably a blessing. Not sure I could have coped with two disapproving sisters. Appropriately enough, Rose, Katie and I were in a steam room as I confessed to those particular sins. I think maybe if I was Catholic I would have said a few Hail Mary's on my way out. I did notice that Rose had her Mother Superior face on when we emerged from the dark and steamy atmosphere. But I hadn't finished in the confessional... Exchanging the steam room for the Greek Herbal, I continued.

'So, after I gave fat bloke the heave-ho - no mean feat I can tell you - I went back to nights out with Carolyn from work. That's when I met Nico. (How apt that we were in the Greek Herbal Room as Nico, as the name suggested, was of Greek descent.) Carolyn and I had been happily people watching in Wetherspoons while topping up our vodka levels before going on to a club. Unbeknown to us, two guys were watching us watching everyone else. God, I hope they weren't making the same sort of bitchy comments. Anyway, we finally spotted these two guys and they weren't the usual spotty oiks found in Wetherspoons so we agreed to join them for a drink. Nico and Pete seemed like really great guys and, after a couple more drinks, we all went on to the nightclub together. The club was called 'The Beach' and I wondered if it was sign. Well, yes it was of course. In bright neon letters above the door. Not that sort of sign, silly. An omen type sign.

'Nico and Carolyn were soon an item on the dance floor and I found myself getting close to Pete. Close to his mouth to be precise. My God, I think it was the best snog I ever had. Nothing more happened between any of us that night, but we all exchanged phone numbers and agreed to keep in touch. Trouble was, that as far as I was concerned, I'd been touching the wrong guy. I really liked Pete – boy, could he kiss – but I didn't fancy him. Nico, on the other hand, was really cute. I'm not sure if I should use the word 'cute' to describe a man, but it's true, he was.

'It turned out that Nico felt the same way – the wrong couples had hooked up that night. So, there I was again, sowing away like mad with another younger man. Life was good. But I felt bad. I knew that Pete liked me and I felt a little as though we were betraying him. We didn't tell him what went on between us for a long time – but that's another of those whole other stories. Nico and I kept it casual (I think nowadays we'd be called "Friends with Benefits") as he'd been badly hurt by an ex and I wasn't looking for anything serious. I didn't feel too bad when the time came to end the 'relationship'. Looking back, I hope I didn't hurt Nico by assuming it was casual for him too. You know they say to assume 'makes an ass of u and me'. Just me in this case perhaps. Little did I know what was to happen on a certain weekend away during that whole other story. Just maybe there would be a happy ending for Nico.'

After a blissful day at the spa Katie and I returned home refreshed and relaxed and vowing to remain in this calm state for as long as possible. I think I managed about forty five minutes. Kids. Who'd have 'em?

34

Surgical spirit

'D-day' (or 'Double D-day' as Ali had suggested after I told her that was the cup size the surgeon was aiming for) was approaching rapidly, and my fears about the surgery were going from a simmer to a rapid boil. The big red circle around August the seventeenth was looming large on the calendar hanging on the kitchen wall. I was finding it increasingly hard to remain calm with the boys when they were less than obedient (which was most of the time) and feeling guilty about leaving Tom with assorted friends and family while I was in hospital. I think the unusually hot summer was also making me extra grouchy.

Before DD-day, however, I had one more hurdle to clear: the pre-assessment appointment on August the third, which would determine once and for all if I was fit enough, and indeed light enough, to have the operation. Well if I wasn't before, I thought, I sure as hell would be after the op; my new boobs would be truly WAG-worthy. (I hope I didn't regret saying WAG and ended up with the dreaded dog ears.)

The pre-assessment day was just another exercise in humiliation really. Along with a barrage of blood tests and questions, I was weighed and measured. And photographed.

'OK, Lucy, if you could just strip to your knickers please,' the medical photographer asked.

'Of course,' I said, obliging as ever, but secretly wishing I could be anything but. I wasn't one of those women comfortable with flashing my boobs. I'd never had the courage even to sunbathe topless.

'Right, now if you could stand in front of the white screen, facing me, arms down by your sides.'

'Go to your happy place, Lucy,' I muttered to myself, as I followed the instruction. God, this was so embarrassing. Unfortunately, it was raining in my happy place.

'Great,' said the photographer after snapping a couple of full-frontals. 'Now if you could just turn to your right.'

God, I thought, this must be what criminals feel like having their mugshots taken. Only worse, because I'm only guilty of having enormous boobs which, as far as I was aware, was not against the law.

'Super. All done,' said the photographer, and my ordeal was at an end.

I said a hurried 'thank you' and scurried off to put my clothes back on, relieved that it was over.

Put it this way, the photos would not be appearing on my Facebook profile any time soon, and any passing thought about glamour modelling had well and truly passed. I just thanked God the medical photographer was a woman. I knew I had to get used to people looking at my chest (after all they'd been gawping at it for years) but I still felt uncomfortable every time a new doctor or nurse had to assess me. I could only imagine what it was going to be like in hospital when they came at me with the marker pen. Still, my surgeon was a woman so it wouldn't be that bad.

Thanks to a few days of dieting, my BMI was suitably low

and my surgery date was finally confirmed for a fortnight's time. I was thrilled to finally be on the home straight, but at the same time terrified of the actual procedure. Just the thought of the anaesthetic filled me with dread, let alone the knowledge that my nipples were going to be cut off, moved a considerable distance before being grafted back on. The way my consultant talked about how far my nipples had to move I wondered if they might be needing passports. At the very least it was going to mean a change of postcodes.

Apparently, the vast distance needing to be traversed by my nipples was the reason I needed 'free nipple grafts' (well I'm buggered if I'd pay for the privilege) rather than having them left on a stalk. Either option sounded completely gross, so I consoled myself with the thought that I would be asleep throughout the great nipple expedition. Only when I woke up would I give myself permission to worry about whether or not the grafts would take. I really couldn't cope with the thought of nipple necrosis without losing my lunch, and I was pretty sure my low-fat, low-sugar, low-salt, low-taste bean soup would be pretty damned disgusting coming back up. It had been bad enough going down. (I have always found chocolate button puddings to be the most desirable thing to eat if you think you are likely to be sick.)

I attempted to take my mind off the decidedly gruesome thought of dead nipples by thinking about all the new clothes and underwear I could buy. Another reason for a fundraiser methinks. All those pretty bras I could buy, from high street stores instead of the local marquee company. Lacy bras, T-shirt bras, balconette bras, Wonderbras even. The bra world would be my oyster. Peephole bras, I thought. Hmmm. Maybe not such a good idea if my nipples fell off. But still, the fashion world suddenly seemed almost accessible and I couldn't wait to wear clothes which I could only dream of before. Bring on the scalpel.

35

Nemesis

Before my op I had a long overdue night out with Ali, and the annual holiday with Paul's family.

I'd accepted an invitation to birthday drinks for a girl I knew vaguely from my old job and we had several friends in common, one of whom was Ali. I'd been trying to catch up with Ali for ages so it seemed like the perfect opportunity to kill two birds with one stone. There was, however, a small flaw in the plan, a fly in the ointment if you will. My old adversary Freya was going to be there. Eek. I hadn't seen her for years and was really anxious about how seeing her again would make me feel. I wasn't sure if it was such a good idea, but decided that it was a necessary part of the healing process of a sore that had never really fully healed.

I made a big effort to look my best that night. I think I looked OK and Ali seemed suitably impressed:

'Wow, Lucy, you look amazing! Freya's going to be gobsmacked.'

'Thanks, Ali. I have to admit, though, I'm dreading facing Freya. I really don't know how seeing her again will feel. I don't want to fall apart in front of everyone.'

'You won't – I won't let you!'

Ali, my rock in a crisis once again, I thought as a picture of her squeezing through the pantry window during the locked-out-of-the-house-drama flashed into my mind.

She hadn't seen me since I'd lost weight and started to feel a bit better about myself and was amazed to see the old Lucy emerging butterfly-like from a cocoon of fat. I felt good, if ever so slightly terrified. And not just about seeing Freya. I was wearing heels for the first time in absolutely ages and was worried I might fall arse over enormous tits in front of everyone. Also, I was driving and was therefore going to have to endure the whole experience stone cold sober. With hindsight this was probably just as well, as I don't think I would've been nearly so dignified under the influence.

I was quaking in my stilettos as Ali and I walked into the pub. Ali gave my hand a reassuring squeeze. I saw Freya straight away and was almost too scared to acknowledge her, but I tried to be mature about the whole thing.

'Hello Freya,' I managed to utter, in between unsteady breaths. At that point I thought I might have to run to the ladies to throw up, but I took a deep breath to steady myself and looked to Ali for courage. Thank goodness she was there. No way could I have done this on my own.

'Hello, Lucy,' Freya said, with a smile that didn't reach her eyes and a decidedly sheepish look on her face. I immediately had the feeling that there was something I didn't know.

'How are you?' I asked politely. What I really wanted to ask was how Dan was.

'I'm good thanks. Working in HR now,' Freya couldn't look me in the eyes. She didn't ask how I was.

I couldn't bring myself to ask after Dan directly. I didn't want her to think I still cared, but my heart was in my mouth as we continued to make small talk. More tiny talk, really. I told her about my forthcoming operation and she said she also needed a breast reduction because her boobs got in the way when she had golf lessons. My heart bled. I found her superficial and wondered why we had ever been friends. I enjoyed seeing her scowl as more and more people arrived and told me how fantastic I looked, while ignoring her. Freya was clearly uncomfortable talking to me and I couldn't help feeling that she was hiding something.

That something turned out to be that she and Dan had split up some six months earlier. I didn't find this out from Freya mind you, but from another old colleague. I didn't know why Freya and Dan had split, but I had my suspicions. I left the pub with very mixed feelings.

As we drove out of the pub car park, Ali turned to me: 'You OK, Luce?'

'Yes. No. I don't know. Confused, I think.'

'That's understandable in the circumstances, I'd say.'

I could feel a lump growing in my throat, and tears prickling in the corners of my eyes. I felt a bit shaky and my hands tightened on the steering wheel. I was driving on a dark and unfamiliar road, and needed to hold it together.

Ali, ever sensitive to my feelings, saw I was a bit wobbly.

'Do you need to stop somewhere?'

'No, I'm ok. Sorry, Ali, I think it's just a reaction to the stress of seeing Freya. And finding out that she and Dan have split up. I'm ashamed to say that I'm pleased that they've separated.'

'You're only human. I'd feel the same.'

'I don't think Freya ever really loved him. I've never understood why they got together in the first place. But all the time they were married it somehow justified what Freya did to me.'

'Well, you know what I think of Freya. I've never trusted her; never understood why the two of you were friends – you're nothing like each other.'

'Well, if it's any consolation, after tonight, I've reached the same conclusion. I am most definitely not missing anything by not being friends with Freya.'

After I had dropped Ali off, hugging each other as best we could in the confines of the car, I drove home wondering what might have been. What if I hadn't left my job? What if I had listened to my instincts when I first met Freya? What if what if what if? She'd destroyed our friendship to be with Dan, and now she'd hurt him too. It all seemed so pointless.

I knew I had to compose myself before I got home, so I took a deep breath and checked my face in the rear view mirror, wiping away a few mascara-stained tear tracks. My happy face was plastered back on my face by the time I opened the front door.

36

a Norfolk broad

The next day we were heading to Norfolk for a week of August sunshine (ever the optimist). The annual holiday with Paul's family included his parents, along with his brother and sister and their partners and children. I was looking forward to a break after all the recent stress. And, although we'd have eight children, ranging in age from one to twelve, with us, it would still be a change. And don't they say that a change is as good as a rest? Yes, it would undoubtedly be stressful at times with sixteen of us under one roof, but it would be different stress. I was hoping we would get some sunshine and be able to head for the beach. I'd be able to give my ginormous bikini one last outing before it went on the ceremonial bonfire. I would probably need to have the fire brigade on stand-by for that particular conflagration.

We'd arranged for a friend to call in and feed the cats once a day and to give Louie his tablet every other day. The vet had decided it was time to wean the neurotic one off his anti-depressants and I was a little anxious about how he would cope without me for a week. I will also admit to being worried about my curtains. What if he reverted to his alter ego and Le Wee reclaimed his territory? No amount of Urine-Off or Febreze was going to help after a week of Le Wee on the le-oose. I wondered if there was such a thing as The Priory for felines with addictions, and found myself singing 'we tried to make him go to re-hab, but he said miaow, miaow, miaow'. Get a grip, woman. He'll be fine. Just hide all the sharp implements and give him the phone number for the Samari-cats.

So it was, with some trepidation, that we set off for Norfolk. I just hoped that Louie would cooperate and take his tablets. I didn't like to think of him going cold turkey. Marmite might eat him. Once we were on the motorway, I gave myself a mental shake and tried to put my pet worries to the back of my mind, where they could fester for the next seven days. Much like a mouse carcass lying undetected for a week.

The weather was kind to us on our first day in Norfolk and we packed up buckets and spades and the correct number of children and headed for Cromer beach. Cromer seemed some-how appropriate for my excessively ample boobs to make their final appearance as I had spent many a happy holiday there as a child. (Minus the enormous chest, naturally.) It was a place I had fond mammories of and I wasn't surprised when everyone else fell in love with the jewel of the North Norfolk coast.

Being at a seaside resort also gave me a chance to feed my gambling addiction. I was absolutely hooked on the two-pence machines and would ram coins into the slots like a woman possessed, desperately trying to win cheap toys, key-rings and badges for the children. It didn't matter that these toys were of the poorest quality and would probably last all of five minutes if played with: I had to win at all costs. And the costs were great. I could've bought decent toys with the money I wasted on those damned machines, but where was the buzz in that? A double shot of espresso before going to the toy shop might have done the trick, but nothing could replicate the disgustingly dirty fingertips you got from handling all those two-pence pieces. Hmmm. Gamblers Anonymous might just be getting a call from me sometime soon…

Our holiday home was an amazing old house with four-poster beds and uneven floors. It oozed character and sometimes it oozed bits of plaster on you if someone was walking around on the floor above. It also boasted a small heated indoor swimming pool, which was a big hit with the children. Tom hadn't been swimming for a year due to his having had umpteen colds and ear infections, so I wasn't sure how he would take to the pool. While he still wasn't exactly a merboy in water, Tom loved the pool and felt safe wearing his Day-Glo orange arm bands. I was amazed when, on only the second day, he went in with only a long 'noodle' float. He was doing brilliantly and I was so proud of him. Especially as I had never learnt to swim, or overcome my fear of being out of my depth. (And not just where water was concerned.)

On the third day, Paul decided it would be a good idea to take Tom's noodle away. On day four, Tom was back in his arm bands. Need I say more?

I was banished from the pool room after that. Tom's grandad John had seen the horror on my face when my poor baby went under the water and had uttered just two words: 'Lucy. Out.' He knew that the presence of an overprotective mum was only going to make matters worse. Dads and grandads are much less emotional and highly-strung when it comes to things like child safety. I knew deep down that Tom wasn't in any real danger, but I vowed that, when we returned from holiday, Tom would be enrolled in swimming lessons, ear infection or not.

The rest of the holiday was largely uneventful, apart from

Grandma locking herself in the bathroom at least once a day. I really should have told her sooner that there was a knack to that particular lock, but it was terribly funny listening to her trying to get out. I also took the opportunity to share a childhood song with the kids:

'Oh dear, what can the matter be?
Two old ladies stuck in the lavatory,
They've been there from Monday to Saturday,
Nobody knew they were there.'

They didn't let me down and had soon adapted it to 'poor old Grandma'. We also celebrated Tom's sixth birthday and I made another mental note to teach him about when it's OK to tell a lie. i.e. when someone gives you a present you don't like. Oh the innocence of youth which allows you to always tell it as you see it, and the other person's feelings be damned. After a certain age telling the truth is likely to land you with a smack in the mouth. Although this was not the approach I would be taking with Tom. Not yet anyway.

After the holiday I needed a holiday, so I was actually quite looking forward to a few days in hospital. Lots of peace and quiet and time to read or doze or just be. Sounded perfect. Oh what a rude awakening I was in for.

My final few days with enormous boobs were spent at home with Tom, and his half-brothers, Jamie and Scott. Paul had to work so that he could take time off while I was in hospital. In some ways, it was easier with all three boys as the older two kept Tom occupied. Admittedly, this occasionally meant all hell broke loose as play-fighting turned into real fighting, but this was still preferable to my having to play Transformers for hours on end. No matter how hard I tried to follow the instructions I could never transform the damn things correctly. I really hoped my surgeon was better at following instructions than me, and that my transformation was more successful than my attempts with Optimus Prime et al.

I have to admit that the boys did make me laugh quite a lot that week, and, when I wasn't screaming at them like a fish-wife, we had some good times. I particularly remember bugs being a big thing that summer. Not the mini beasts themselves of course. They were pretty tiny on the whole. Apart from 'Trigger' that is.

Trigger was an enormous slug and Jamie decided he'd make a good pet, as I discovered when I found him in a shoe box on the dining table. Jamie had made a mini garden in the box and Trigger had taken up residence. I did suggest that Jamie ought to call the slug 'Winnie' as it looked like a big poo. Now, I'm not a big fan of slugs, but even so, I was concerned that Trigger would dry out if Jamie kept him for too long. But Jamie had already thought of that and produced a water pistol to keep conditions nice and moist in Slugsville. Round one to Jamie. Ding ding, round two:

'What if one of the cats finds him? I wouldn't put it past either of them to eat a slug. After all, they're quite happy to eat their own sick,' I said, trying to sound concerned.

'Don't worry,' countered Jamie. 'I've got some net to put over the box.'

'Oh good,' I said. *Oh bugger*, I thought.

I did, however, ask that Jamie keep Trigger in a shady spot in the garden and after a few hours, I insisted that Trigger wasn't happy and persuaded Jamie that the kindest thing would be to let the slug go. Thankfully he didn't ask how I could tell a slug looked unhappy.

After Trigger came a multitude of other wee beasties and miniature gardens complete with ponds and ornaments. It was good clean fun (apart from the dirt) and just the sort of thing little boys ought to be doing in the summer holidays I thought to myself. Enid Blyton would've been proud.

Scott and Tom had their moments too. Scott made me laugh when we realised that the reason he wouldn't try eating liver was that he thought it came from humans. One of Tom's finer moments came when we saw a programme on meerkats and the narrator was talking about the new litter:

'Meerkats are allowed rubbish!' he exclaimed in disbelief. (He'd been lectured from an early age about not leaving litter.)

The only real lows of the week were also animal-related. Marmite and Louie decided to carry out a mouse massacre and for a few days I was finding bits of dead mouse everywhere and having to clean little bloody patches of carpet. Bloody cats. Then, something went wrong with the heater in the aquarium and all our fish got boiled alive. I was terribly upset when I discovered what had happened and I broke the news gently to Tom who was sure to be equally devastated:

'Mummy's got some very sad news, Tom,' I began.

'Can I see the bodies?' was Tom's only concern when I broke the news. Followed by 'Can we feed them to the cats?' I needn't have worried about that then I thought as I fished out the bodies of our dearly departed fishy friends. I had been considering burying them in the garden and having a little headstone and a funeral, but as Tom really wasn't bothered I just wrapped them up in a carrier bag and chucked them in the dustbin. Well, the cats might have dug them up if I *had* buried them in the garden.

37

They had me in stitches

The big red circle on the calendar had been reached and, as I lay in my hospital bed down in East Grinstead, my earlier excitement was rather dampened by the sheer terror which had washed over me along with the knowledge that the next morning would see me in theatre and at the needle point of no return. Mamma mia! Might be the last time my nipples were at the point of anything, I thought morosely.

I was on a ward with three other women and we soon got talking about why we were in hospital. It's amazing how four complete strangers can share deeply personal information so quickly. I suppose we immediately had something in common and somehow, being in your night clothes in a hospital bed, makes everyone equal. Whatever your age, background, marital status, sexual preferences and favourite crisp flavour, this is one of those situations which levels out the playing field. Before the night was over we four women would know more about each other than the closest of friends, and I would be humbled by the strength and courage of womankind.

Although I knew from past experience that first impressions can prove wholly inaccurate, I still concluded that one particular middle-aged woman called Veronica was rather snobby and stand-offish. That was until she changed into a Snoopy night-shirt and gave us a flash of the markings made by her surgeon to show the area of flesh which was to be removed from her shoulder to reconstruct her breast. There I was in my new M&S pyjamas and matching dressing gown, bought especially to go into hospital, waiting to have my breasts voluntarily reduced. I felt almost ashamed when I admitted why I was sharing ward space with this brave and long-suffering lady. I might as well have just said, 'Well, ladies, my boobs are just too big!'

One thing I learnt during my time in hospital (apart from the fact that hospital veterans don't waste their money on new night wear for the occasion) was that breast cancer is an evil and devious disease which affects the sufferer's life almost indefinitely. And that the women who are affected by it endure it with courage and humour. I asked them to get all the gags over before my op the next morning as I was quite sure that while laughing might well be the best medicine, it was gonna hurt like hell with all those stitches.

The woman in the bed opposite me, Tracey, was in for nipple reconstruction; another step on the long road to recovery. Tracey wasn't much older than me and had already endured a double mastectomy which had left her chest concave. She went on to explain what the next stage of her journey entailed.

'So, because I'm so slim, I had to have implants after my mastectomy and the skin on my chest is just too tight for them to make nipples, so they're having to go elsewhere for flesh to model my new ones.' Tracey was so calm and matter-of-fact as she described in graphic detail the horrors she continued to face.

Elsewhere turned out to be her labia. Not only was she going to have new nipples, but a designer vagina into the bargain. We all had a good giggle about it, but the thought of what her op entailed made my stomach turn over as I crossed, not only my legs, but my arms protectively across my chest. Tracey, like Veronica, seemed to be taking it all in her stride and was able to laugh about the whole ghastly prospect. By this time I had a severe case of what can only be described as 'survivor's guilt', but Tracey soon had me laughing again as she described the prosthetic nipples she had been given to try. Apparently they would have made great tea towel hangers.

The third lady on the ward, Val, was having a mastectomy. I couldn't begin to imagine how she must be feeling. I felt another surge of guilt as I listened to her cancer story. I wondered about the tact, or lack thereof, of putting someone like me in with three breast cancer patients. It did seem rather insensitive towards them – rather like women who have had miscarriages being in a maternity ward amongst new mothers and their babies. A cruel rubbing of salt in a horrendous wound.

Sleep eluded me that night (peace and quiet did not, I discovered, exist in hospital) and I aimlessly wandered the corridors, just waiting for sunrise and trying to ignore the rumblings coming from my stomach. I had been nil by mouth since midnight and was starting to worry about my blood sugar. I was too preoccupied to read and it was a relief when eight o'clock in the morning finally arrived, and with it my consultant. Make that consultant plus one. That one being a young man called Simon. Oh bugger. It transpired that I was to be operated on by two surgeons, one for each breast. I prayed silently that they didn't have completely different surgical styles and that I would be left with at least vaguely matching boobs. I really didn't want my boob job boobed. Simon was a registrar in need of a bit of practice, but my consultant assured me that she would be there every step of the way.

Then came the dreaded marker pen.

I hadn't really thought about why the pen marks had to be made while I was conscious and upright. But, apparently, it wasn't just to cause me further embarrassment. No, it was so that when I was lying down and my enormous knockers obeyed the laws of gravity the surgeons would still be able to tell where to cut. I had visions of an extra gurney on either side of my bed, one per breast. Oh God. More embarrassment. I thought they would use some kind of special marker pen designed for use on skin. In reality it was just your bog standard black marker and the registrar proceeded to start marking me up as he thought appropriate. Now and then Miss Zahari would step in and make a slight correction. I half expected her to use a red pen and give Simon a mark out of ten. I began to worry that they wouldn't know which lines to cut along as I started to resemble some kind of novice dressmaker's pattern. Simon drew what looked like targets to represent the new positions for my nipples. I was somewhat comforted that he didn't ask if they had their tickets and passports and if they'd packed their own luggage. Even better, he didn't ask if I'd bought new tea towels lately.

Before long, I was in my lovely backless hospital gown (definitely not designer) and surgical stockings (mmm sexy) and being wheeled to theatre. I have to admit I'd rather have been in a cocktail dress and fishnets in the West End, but as this was one performance I was going to sleep through, I supposed it didn't really matter what I wore. I'd never had an anaesthetic (not counting the self-induced vodka variety) before and didn't know what to expect or how I was going to react to one. I was already disappointed not to have been given a pre-med and arrived in theatre in a delightful daze. Maybe they were reserved for private patients and the truly hysterical. I'd remember that for next time.

When the anaesthetist finally managed to insert a cannula into my uncooperative vein, I expected to have to count backwards from ten before slipping into a deep sleep. Well, that's what happened on television. Instead he said I would start to feel light-headed. Nothing happened for a couple of seconds, apart from panic, but then the next thing I knew someone was saying my name and I was waking up in recovery. I felt OK. Hurrah! I had been convinced I would be throwing up everywhere and have a splitting headache when I came round. But I felt fine. Yippee. It was over.

Famous last words. A couple of hours later I was being violently sick and had the mother of all migraines. Apparently it's not uncommon to have a delayed reaction to an anaesthetic. I felt absolutely wretched as I retched into yet another bowl, passed to me by the nurse at one end of the chain gang of nurses ferrying used and new dishes at a rate of knots. In between bouts of vomiting I uttered a feeble apology to my fellow ward-mates. This went on for about twenty-four hours, with the staff desperately trying to stop the vomiting long enough to keep pain-killers down. Talk about a vicious cycle. I was given drug after drug, one to counteract another, trial and error all the way. But mostly error. It turned out I'm allergic to codeine, don't react well to morphine, and can't take ibuprofen or aspirin as they cause abdominal pain. God, I'd be useless as a junkie.

To add to my misery I had to be put on a drip to replace the lost fluids. Again my veins refused to cooperate and I started to feel like a pin cushion. It was a challenge not to get tangled up in all the tubes coming out of me: I also had them coming out of my chest to drain away any excess blood. The staff had kindly provided me with a pillow case to carry around my bottles of blood should I ever feel well enough to get out of bed. At this point, however, getting out of bed seemed about as likely as a bouquet of roses and a get well card arriving from Danny Campbell.

The physiotherapist apparently had other ideas and the very next day I was given a sheet of exercises to do three times a day. She was clearly some kind of sadistic nutter if she expected me to lift my arms above my head. I could barely lift my cup of tea when I finally stopped throwing up, and had thought about asking for a straw. The slightest movement felt as though I would rupture something.

'Stitches are very strong,' the physio assured me.

Easy for you to say, I thought – it won't be your nipples flying off *Carry on Camping* style. Tracey wouldn't believe her luck.

Not wanting to be told off, I dutifully attempted to raise my arms sufficiently to satisfy the psycho physio and promised to do a little bit more every day. I must have an honest face as she left me alone after that. I'm sure she knew what she was talking about, but I was terrified every time I moved as it really felt that something was going to split open. Not for the first time I wondered why anyone would undergo surgery for purely cosmetic reasons. It was the experience from hell and I was having a devil of a time believing I'd ever feel well again.

Of course I did eventually get out of bed after the humiliation of using a bed pan or commode got the better of me. Once I was off the drip, I managed to manoeuvre my drain pipes and bottles of blood into the pillow case and toddle off to the toilet. I wondered idly if said bottles would ultimately find their way to some kind of vampire blood bar. Seemed a terrible waste of perfectly good blood otherwise.

It was a huge relief when, after forty-eight hours, the drains were finally removed. I say relief, but having the tubes pulled out was one of the most uncomfortable experiences of my life.

'Just take three deep breaths, dear, and then I'll ease the tubes out,' instructed the nurse who was going to remove the tubes. Eased was definitely the wrong word as there was nothing easy about it. As I took the third breath, the nurse tugged on the tubes. They didn't budge and the discomfort was considerable. 'Right, they do seem to be a little more reluctant to come out than usual. Let's try again. Big breaths.'

I had to giggle, despite the pain, as I fought back the urge to say, 'Not anymore!'

With a bit of jiggling, the tubes finally came out and, once those harrowing few seconds were over, I felt loads better and was able to move about much more easily. As long as that movement didn't involve lifting my arms, breathing hard, coughing, getting in and out of bed or any number of other everyday actions.

My relief was compounded when I was told on day four I could go home. Being in hospital hadn't been quite the relaxing sojourn I had anticipated. Sleep, if it ever came, was interrupted by nurses taking the necessary observations at regular intervals; morning tea arrived before morning; and I was too preoccupied to read to before surgery and in too much pain afterwards. To cap it all, my lovely new M&S pyjamas had blood on them. Veronica's Snoopy nightshirt now made perfect sense. I would know for next time. If there ever was a next time. Which I fervently hoped there would not be. Only time would tell if the dreaded revision surgery would be needed to tidy up any loose ends.

Once home, I took up residence in the spare room and surrounded myself with pillows in an attempt to get comfortable. The thought of anyone trying to cuddle up to me was not a nice one, and I didn't think I could endure sharing a bed with tsunami-man just yet. I secretly wondered how long I could justify sleeping in the spare room. Six months sounded reasonable to me. I'm sure Paul would have other ideas, but he'd survive. Tom would just have to understand that he couldn't hug Mummy for a while. I knew he was worried that I wouldn't be 'nuggly' without my ample bosoms and I hoped it wouldn't affect how he felt about me. If need be I wasn't averse to shoving a couple of balloons up my top from time to time to give him some reassurance. Or maybe not. What if that led him to have some weird kind of fetish when he was older? What if one of them burst mid-nuggle? He'd have all sorts of damaging associations with balloons. And breasts. And have to have years of counselling as a result. I could just imagine his therapist asking if he was breast fed…

I guess guilt is a normal side effect of being a parent. I felt bad that Tom had been booked on a three-day football course while I was in hospital. He was going with his best friend Matty (who was equally reluctant) and was having his first sleepover to boot. I just hoped they would enjoy the training once they got there but I had my doubts as Tom is not really the sporty type. I have a feeling that in years to come he'll be using his head for things other than scoring goals. I heard afterwards from Sarah that day one of football school had been a long and tiring one and that neither of the boys wanted to go on the second day. Tom apparently did his best to get out of it by announcing that he and Matty were actually allergic to grass and therefore could not go. In a stroke of genius, Sarah consulted an imaginary list of allergies I'd given to her and told Tom that grass wasn't on it. It seemed that Tom had met his match. It probably wouldn't be the only match he'd lose that day.

Putting my worries and guilt about Tom aside I concentrated on my recovery. To be fair it didn't require much concentration. Doing nothing but eat, sleep, read, watch television, eat, nap, was really pretty straightforward. And boring. The highlight of my day was having a shower. That was the only time I was allowed to take off my sports bra. My wounds were still taped up so I didn't see the state of my patchwork breasts for a while. I looked forward to the great unveiling with a mixture of emotions. Would it hurt when they took the dressings off? Would I be happy with the result? Would I be upset when I saw what they'd done to me? Would my nipples fall off and I'd have to have tea towel hooks stuck on? It was such a big adjustment (two kilos to be exact) and I was still getting used to being able to see my feet when I looked down. Although admittedly I could see rather too much tummy before my feet came into view. On my bad days I did wonder if they'd given me tummy implants while I was under. Waste not want not and all that. Or, in this case, waist not want not.

Dressing removal day came and went and was rather an anti-climax. I realise, as a woman, I should be used to these. The surgeon whipped the dressings off with minimal discomfort, declared everything satisfactory and said she'd see me in four months' time. I was then re-packaged and sent away without even so much as a glance in a mirror. The nurses said they didn't have a mirror, but I think it was just a cunning way of avoiding having to deal with any hysterics when patients saw their mutilated breasts for the first time. I was told to remove the dressings once and for all in the shower after one week. Why in the shower I wondered? So no-one could hear me scream? Or to ensure that any bits which fell off were safely caught in the plug hole? Or so that I didn't get any mess on the carpet?

These questions would remain unanswered for the next seven days. One thing that didn't go unanswered was the doorbell. Every time someone new came to the house and tried desperately not to look at my chest I wanted to die of embarrassment. It was such a dramatic change and everyone who saw me was clearly gobsmacked and wanted a good gawp but didn't want to be offensive. I didn't look forward to the day when my new chest and I had to put in an appearance in the school playground at the start of term.

My surgeon had given me the all-clear to drive which was a relief as it meant I could do the school runs at the start of term. Getting Tom to and from school would have been a logistical nightmare otherwise. I just hoped I wouldn't have to do an emergency stop any time soon. The thought of my seat belt pulling tight across my chest was not a pleasant one. I have to confess to putting a cushion under my seat belt for the first few days though. Just in case. I did contemplate shoving the cushion up my jumper to put off the moment of revelation.

Walking into school that first morning was interesting to say the least. Those that knew about the op were curious to see the result, and those that didn't were obviously trying to work out what was different about me. I looked about six inches taller now that the weight of my breasts wasn't pulling me forwards like the hunchback of Notre Dame. I also looked a lot slimmer now that I had rediscovered my ribcage. I felt a million times more confident and it showed. It was just a shame that underneath the clothes I looked like Frankenstein's monster, as I was to discover when I finally took my dressings off.

I say when *I* took the dressings off, but that's not strictly accurate. I dutifully went in the shower and attempted to peel the tape off. And failed miserably. I had to call Paul to come and assist with their removal. It felt horrid as the tapes were peeled away from the wounds and I have to admit to shedding a few tears when I first saw myself in the mirror. My breasts were like a badly-stitched patchwork quilt and I couldn't imagine ever feeling attractive again. Paul tried to reassure me but I think what I was feeling was entirely natural and it was a case of time heals all. It was very early days and I just had to be patient. The fact that I did indeed have one of the dreaded dog-ears didn't help. It was possible I would need revision surgery, but it was just too soon to tell.

I tried to console myself with the fact that my nipples were still attached, even though one was considerably larger than the other. I guess my surgeons had different ideas of what was attractive. I had named my breasts after the two doctors who had done the surgery. The right one was now called Simon and the left Anita. It was Simon who'd gone with the big nipple. I can't think about my nipples for too long at any one time as it makes me cringe to think of them being sliced off and popped to one side while two kilos of breast tissue was removed. Someone pass the sick bowl. Let the weight loss continue.

Nipples aside, I was thrilled to be rid of my old boobs. I hadn't realised quite how much they'd been dragging me down. Physically and mentally. Paul was surprised at how much he liked the new smaller me. As a self-confessed boob-man he had been apprehensive about the reduction. Tom didn't seem to miss the nuggly boobs too much either, which was even more of a relief. I think Paul was looking forward to clothes and underwear shopping as much as me.

38

Ladies who Lurch

It was soon after my surgery that I heard from Jess. She'd been living and working in China for a couple of years, and we'd kept in touch on Facebook Messenger:

'Hey, Lucy Loo!' she'd written. 'I have news. I'm a comin' home!'

'Really? Oh my God, that's wonderful! I have soooo missed you.'

'It is wonderful, but it's also a bit rubbish – turns out I have a heart murmur. Coming back for the UK docs to take a look.'

'Oh jeez, Jess. I'm so sorry! I can't believe it!'

'I know, right. Couldn't be something simple like having enormous boobs!' she joked. You could always rely on Jess to make light of a situation and try to turn the attention away from her. 'How are the new boobs by the way?'

In light of Jess's revelation, the new boobs were just fine thank you very much. She wasn't getting off the hook that easily.

'Forget my boobs, young lady. I want details.'

'Ooh when did you get so bossy, Luce?' Jess continued to joke.

'I'm serious, Jess, I want to know what's happening with you.'

'OK, OK, so apparently I've got a faulty valve and it probably needs replacing. No biggie.'

No biggie?! That was like saying my 32K chest was 'no biggie'

196

before Simon and Anita whittled it down to a D cup.

'Christ on a bike! You poor thing. I want to come to the hospital with you.'

'Why? To check for hot doctors? I'll be fine. Mum and Dad are gonna want to take me anyhoo.'

'OK, but we have to catch up as soon as poss. And you have to let me know if I can do anything, Jess. I mean it, anything at all.' I was really worried about my fearless young friend.

'Absolutely! We need a long overdue catch up and night out. I want to see the new, improved you.'

I assumed (naively) that the night out would be a quiet meal somewhere, with sparkling water and an early finish. Silly me! Jess wasn't going to let some dodgy heart valve cramp her style. She really believed that life was to be lived in the fast lane, and nothing would slow her down. (Except maybe the men she dated.)

Jess was fourteen years my junior, but she had more life experience than anyone I knew and had an old head on those young shoulders. One side effect of said old head was a penchant for older men. And when I say older, I mean it's OK if they have a free bus pass. While the rest of us think of wrinkly old bits and a need for Viagra, Jess sees a wealth of experience and maturity that she didn't find in younger men.

Now, while I don't think of myself as ageist, I much prefer the idea of a toy boy. Not so young that I could have given birth to him, but quite a bit younger would be fine. On the plus side, this did mean that if we ever went out on the pull, we'd never be competing for the same man. However, it also meant that Jess didn't want to work it with my toy boy's mate, and I didn't want to take off with her old fella's wing man. The only way we were going to have any success on a night out was if a good-looking thirty-year-old was out with his dad. This was of course irrelevant as I was married and Jess had left behind an OAP in China. But that didn't mean we couldn't look. So, once I finally got out of my sports bra and Jess had seen the cardiac specialist, we arranged a night out to do just that.

I hadn't had a girly night out for ages and, worse still, I hadn't drunk for years. I was really worried about how the alcohol would affect me. I'd either fall asleep or spend the night with my head down the toilet. Neither was a particularly appealing prospect. I was determined to give it a go though and vowed to go easy on the booze and to drink plenty of water. Or other clear liquid. There was no way I could keep up with a seasoned pro like Jess, but I'd just have to give it my best shot. (Preferably not the Aftershock variety.)

Before the big night out, Jess and I met up for coffee and shopping. We both needed to find suitable outfits to wear, and Jess said there was something she wanted to talk to me about. We met for coffee at a Designer Outlet Centre in Ashford and, over lattés, Jess admitted that she'd met up with my old nemesis Freya earlier in the week. I'd never expected Jess and Tara to take sides over what had happened with Freya and Dan, but I guess they felt a bit awkward about the whole thing. After all, we'd all been close for a while, and, while they didn't approve of what Freya had done, she was still their friend. Anyway, it turned out that Jess thought I should give Freya another chance.

'I know you saw her before your surgery, and I gather it wasn't the most successful of reunions,' she said, 'but we all make mistakes. And you were so close and such great friends.'

Yeah, that was before she reached down my throat, ripped out my heart and stamped on it, I thought. But Jess did have a point. (Maybe I could poke Freya in the eye with it.) Following a discussion involving clichés such as 'Life's too short to bear a grudge' and 'Keep your friends close, but your enemies closer', I finally agreed to Freya joining us on our night out. Eek.

Knowing that I'd be really nervous about seeing Freya again, I decided to splash out a bit on my outfit. I'd need to look and feel my best to stand any chance of appearing composed. I finally settled on a black leather skirt and red satin blouse. (I was going for sexy but classy. Think I may have ended up with high class hooker.) Jess usually wore black so I was gobsmacked when she fell in love with a girly swirly pink dress that wouldn't have looked out of place at a school prom. She looked absolutely beautiful and was determined to wear this dream dress at least once before she had a ten-inch scar down her sternum. It was really a bit much for a glorified pub crawl so we decided to tell people that we were going to a posh do later that night. Planning to tell lies already – I just knew we'd have whole new personas worked out in no time.

I wasn't convinced that Jess could carry off 'lion tamer', so she settled on a documentary maker for television. Her most recent programme was an exploration of the Chinese sex industry. This I could believe, despite the incongruity of the girly pink dress. As for me? Jess suggested a brothel madam. I wasn't sure whether to be insulted or not. I fell back on the old favourite of a sex therapist (maybe not so different to a madam) whom Jess had consulted while researching her next documentary. I wondered aloud if men made up alter egos to make themselves more interesting on nights out with the lads.

If so, what might they be?

'Escort,' was Jess's opening suggestion.

'I was thinking more along the lines of footballer or city trader.'

What did men think would impress women? It might be an interesting insight into men's (mis)understanding of women. Maybe Jess could do a feature on it. See how believable her fake persona was? I was already lining up her next topic. Feeling old and tired, I wasn't sure I could convince anyone that I was in any way connected to the sex industry. I was quite likely to suggest a nice cup of tea and a night in front of the telly. Still, that might work for some people (i.e. most of the men Jess was likely to fancy).

The night was shaping up to be an interesting one. I told myself that I'd liven up after a couple of drinks. Either that or pass out. Praying it was the former, Jess and I set off for our first watering hole. Actually, make that real ale-ing and vodka-ing hole. Not in the same glass, I hasten to add. I'd decided to stick to clear liquids and not mix my drinks. No water for me then. Oh well. Jess debated whether or not to order a half or a pint as she was trying to live up to her dress. In that case she really ought to have ordered something pink with an umbrella in it. To be honest, standing there in her fairy princess dress with a pint was so wrong it was almost right. Nothing would have completed the outfit more perfectly. Except maybe a pair of wellies. I'd given up trying to dissuade Jess from drinking at all, bearing in mind that she was now on beta blockers for her heart murmur.

'Lucy,' she'd said. 'I've probably had this problem my whole life – I'm not about to let it dictate to me. You know me, I've never done things by halves,' she smiled as she lifted her pint glass for a toast. 'Here's to us, Lucy, and a bloody good night.'

Over our first drink, Jess told me that Freya might not be coming after all. 'Apparently, she's met some new man, and might be going out with him.'

That'd be right, I thought. She'd had a better offer and we'd moved down the pecking order. Either that or she was just too chicken.

'Could you text her and find out for sure if she's coming or not?' I asked Jess. I wasn't going to be able to relax otherwise. Deep down, I already knew that the answer would be no. Sure enough, Freya blew us out for a man. Some things never change, I thought. Freya will never put her girlfriends first when there's a man involved. No matter whose man, I added bitchily. Although I will admit to feeling some disappointment, it was mixed with relief that I wouldn't have to confront some extremely painful memories. I resolved to just have a good night with Jess, and raised my glass in another toast.

After a couple more drinks Jess and I realised we had attracted the attention of two guys across the room. I think I probably owned shoes older than them. They definitely came under the 'could have given birth to them' limit and, as they weren't accompanied by their grandfathers (or much, much, much older brothers), Jess was less than enthusiastic. We decided to beat a hasty retreat. As we made our escape, one of the twelve-year-olds called out to us: 'You don't know what you're missing, ladies.' I don't know what was more amusing: the idea that he believed he had something which would impress us, or the fact that he had called us ladies.

We were still giggling when we tottered into the next likely looking pub. Make that unlikely. I felt even more out of place in what turned out to be a bit of a rough establishment. The girls hunted in packs and the guys looked afraid. So they should. You would not want to mess with these women. They meant business. And I don't mean the suited and booted kind. Jess and I were careful not to make eye contact with any of them and took refuge at a corner table. Salubrious was not a word I would have used to describe the furnishings and I think Kim and Aggie from that cleaning show would have had a field day. When I couldn't put off going to the ladies any longer, I didn't need to look for a sign to point the way. The smell led me down a steep stair case, growing ever more pungent and unpleasant as I went. It was quite a way to the toilets and I think that some people may have given up half way and just peed where they stood. In the absence of Kendal Mint Cake I could almost understand how this might happen, but I soldiered on and eventually made it to base camp. I have to admit that I hovered over the loo seat so as not to touch it and opened the door with my elbow. Making a mental note to start carrying alcohol hand gel with me in future, I thought about rubbing some vodka on my hands when I finally regained the summit. I figured the lemonade might make things rather too sticky however, and just hoped I wouldn't contract some unpleasant social disease. Make that anti-social.

It was a relief when we decided to move on and we were careful to go a bit more upmarket with our next choice of bar. This wasn't difficult, admittedly. Jess opened the door and we were relieved not to see sawdust on the floor and the researchers from the Jeremy Kyle show were nowhere to be seen, so we figured we were safe.

Spookily this final bar was full of people wearing wellies. It was someone's fortieth birthday and they had a wigs and wellies theme. Feeling a teensy bit over-dressed I quickly downed another double vodka to take the edge off. That was the one that did it. I could feel it in my eyes; they always got drunk before the rest of me. Now I was ready for anything. Well, at least a bit of a dance anyway. It was really too late to tell people we were going to a posh party later that night, so we had now resorted to saying that we'd just come from said posh party and weren't ready for the night to end just yet. I was amazed to still be conscious by this time. I really thought we'd be back in the B&B in time to see who got voted off *Strictly Come Dancing*. But there I was, after midnight, bopping away on the dance floor and singing along to The Black Eyed Peas - 'I gotta feeling, yeah yeah, that tonight's gonna be a good night' - I may have looked like an embarrassing auntie at a wedding but I was sufficiently tipsy not to care. And if a man young enough to be my nephew wanted to dance with me, then so be it.

It soon became apparent that the bloke celebrating his fortieth birthday found Jess attractive. He seemed like a nice enough guy, but Jess soon dismissed him as boring. I tried to let him down gently on her behalf by explaining that she preferred older men and to try again at his retirement party. He looked confused but seemed to take the hint. Unlike his friend, who kept trying to get us to dance. I did get up and have one dance with him, mainly because I was too polite to say no. Good manners can get you into all sorts of trouble though and I was soon regretting my decision when he starting gyrating next to me like some sort of randy dog about to hump my leg. I made my excuses (politely, of course) and made my way back to Jess.

Randy dog wasn't giving up that easily though and soon came bounding over to try his luck with Jess.

Jess was much better at being a bitch than me. No, I don't mean she let him hump her leg. Just that she didn't believe good manners extended to drunken men who only wanted to get inside your knickers. If she wasn't interested in someone, she made no effort to disguise this fact and wouldn't waste her time on them. Probably very wise really as it eliminated the possibility of mixed signals being given. With not even the sniff of a bone, let alone a titbit, Randy dog was back on his lead and safely kennelled. That was when the puppies arrived.

Jess was at the bar getting a round in and I was sitting on my own trying not to look miserable. I wasn't miserable in the least, just feeling self-conscious being on my own. I thought I was doing OK, but apparently not, as two young men came over and plonked themselves either side of me. They'd taken it upon themselves to cheer me up and I have to say they did a pretty good job. Personally I find it very flattering to be chatted up by much younger men. In this case much younger turned out to be twenty-three. Yes, I was officially old enough to have given birth to them. But rules are made to be broken, aren't they? And it's not as though I was planning to have intercourse with either of them. Both of them, maybe. Only joking. The only intercourse taking place would be of the social variety. Jess didn't look too happy when she got back with our drinks, but I hoped that she'd play nicely. With any luck their dads might be picking them up later. They probably still had homework to do.

They may have been young, but these lads were wise enough to lie about how old they thought I was and look suitably shocked when I told them I was forty-three. Bless their cotton socks. I put all thoughts of my nephews out of my head and let them massage my ego. One of them said he was a physiotherapist, and I wondered if that was his real job or just one he'd chosen for the night. Clever choice if it was: ordinary enough to be believable but showed a certain maturity and indicated that he'd be good with his hands. If only I was twenty years younger, I mused. Oh, and single, of course. Jess was clearly not thinking along similar lines and was looking daggers at me whenever she caught my eye. She had dismissed these young pups as unworthy of her time and wanted them to re-join their litter, most of whom were showing signs of it being past their bedtime.

I, however, was having fun and a nice chat about motherhood, breast reduction surgery (yes, really), and the use of fake personas. Vodka had loosened my tongue nicely. That was the only thing it had loosened I hasten to add. It turns out that men do make up stories about where they're from and what they do for a living, either for a laugh or to impress the ladies, and I managed to get a pretty good selection of those used by my young men in the past:

- *pretending to be Norwegian for twenty minutes* (how wonderfully random)
- '*I work in a pilau rice factory my job is to paint the yellow grains*'
- '*I am a professional balloon racer*'
- '*I go round the country painting electricity pylons grey (because they are black when they are first erected)*'
- '*I used to be a classically-trained concert pianist but then*

I broke my arm in three places (London, Paris and Vienna)
so now I can't reach the very high or very low keys' (whilst
stretching your arms as far as you can in a reaching-the-high-
and-low-keys-on-a-piano movement, clearly showing that you
can in fact still do this)
- 'I am a fighter pilot'

I thought some of these were hilarious, but Jess barely managed a titter. She just couldn't find younger men funny or interesting. Luckily for her, soon after this, the young pups' lift decided he'd had enough excitement for one night and they bounded after him, with a parting 'I think I love you!' from the one who may or may not be a physio. He'd made an old woman very happy, but the time had come for Jess to make an old man very happy, so I sat back while she searched meerkat-style for a suitably wrinkly victim.

In the absence of any geriatrics, Jess had to content herself with a man about my age. A mere whippersnapper, in her opinion, but perhaps worthy of her attention for a while. In no time at all, the conversation had turned to how far you could shoot a ping pong ball with your... er... lady bits, and other delights encountered whilst researching the Chinese sex industry.

Before we knew it, the bouncer was asking us to finish our drinks as it was gone 2 a.m. and they were closing. I couldn't believe I'd gone the distance. More than that, I couldn't believe I'd drunk about fourteen vodkas and was still standing. Hurrah!

Not so hurrah was waking up for breakfast at eight thirty the next morning. Correction. The same morning. Bleurgh. I felt as though as ferret had peed in my mouth. Jess said she felt like she'd swallowed a badger's flip-flop. I suppose these similes were just as valid as 'a mouth like the bottom of a bird cage', even though I had no idea what my mouth would feel like after a ferret had paid a visit to it, and I was quite sure I'd never seen a badger wearing flip-flops. Or indeed any other footwear. I wasn't too worried though as I knew I could go straight back to bed when I got home as Paul was looking after Tom. What a relief.

My relief was short-lived, however, when I arrived home to the news that Paul's parents were coming to visit. I wondered if my in-laws would believe that the alcohol seeping from my pores was really a new body spray and that my lethargy was due to the fact that I was going down with a nasty virus.

39

One of those days

Today was going to be one of those days. You know, *those* days. The ones where everything goes wrong at once. And just when you think nothing else can happen, it bloody well does.

This particular day had gotten off to a pretty ropey start when I dragged myself out of bed to make a cup of tea, only to discover that we'd run out of tea bags. Nooooooooooo! I should have taken this as a sign and gone straight back to bed. This, however, was not an option as Tom had been sick in the night and was off school. I made a cup of instant coffee instead, but it just didn't do the trick. Tea or no tea, I had to strip Tom's bed and mine and wash sicky sheets, duvet covers and pyjamas, and scrub puke-splattered carpets. To cap it all, Marmite had been sick too. She'd developed a delightful habit of throwing up on window sills, somehow managing to achieve a waterfall effect which ensured coverage of sill, wall and carpet. I had a fun-filled day ahead.

Just as I was loading bed sheets into the washing machine, my phone beeped to tell me a text message had been received. It was from Sarah saying that she'd missed us at school this morning and was Tom sick? That would be the understatement of the decade I thought. I filled her in on the latest and she immediately offered to come round with emergency tea bags.

Hurrah! I am saved. Feeling a little better I put on the first of many loads of washing and set off in search of disinfectant.

Another beep. Ooh another text message. News of the humanitarian disaster was spreading and this was no doubt another offer of aid. Or not. It was Sarah to say the road was blocked due to an accident and she couldn't get through with my tea bags. Another sign. Duvet calling. Tom calling. Oh bugger. Having soothed Tom's fevered brow and turned the television over, I headed back to the utility room to resume the hunt for something suitably germ killing. That was when I made the mistake of looking out at the back garden.

There was a big hole where our fence ought to be, and one panel was hanging right over the neighbour's drive. One had disappeared completely. I wondered if I could pretend not to have seen it and let Paul *discover* it when he got home. That's when the doorbell rang. Yes, it was my neighbour. And yes, it was about the fence. Glad that I had a kind and understanding neighbour, I promised to try and remove the offending panel as soon as possible, whilst explaining about sick child, absence of tea bags, etc. The sympathy vote worked beautifully and in a few minutes my neighbour and I had wrestled the fence panel away from the post and dumped it unceremoniously in the garden. They could at least gain access to their house now. The rest would have to wait.

Thanking my neighbour, I headed back indoors to cries of 'Mummy, the telly's gone off'. Along with everything else electrical it seemed. I checked the fuse box, hoping to see a tripped switch just needing to be flicked back on. No such luck. Not today. Today was one of *those* days. It was an RCD that had tripped in the fuse box, and, try as I might, it would not switch back on. I didn't even know what an RCD was, or if I should be touching it, but I had a sick child and television was crucial. I had just left a pathetic message on my electrician's answer phone when, lo and behold, the switch finally allowed itself to be flicked back into the on position. Well that was Sod's Law. The minute I called for help the problem went away. Just like the time when I called out the AA because my car wouldn't start. Yes, you guessed it, the nice man arrived and the car started first time, in spite of the umpteen times it had failed to even spark beforehand. Grrrrrrr. Sodding Sod and his sodding law. He could just sod off.

With Tom resettled in front of the TV, sick bucket at the ready, I took the opportunity to go to the loo. Cue the phone. And the doorbell. That's when the loo roll holder fell off the wall. I was still doing up my jeans as I raced down the stairs to answer the door, but I was expecting a parcel and really didn't want to miss the delivery. God knows what the driver thought I'd been up to when I opened the door breathless and in a state of semi-undress. I made a mental note not to order anything from that particular company again as I scrawled something illegible on the electronic pad the courier held out to me. Checking the missed call on the phone, I realised I'd forgotten to tell the electrician to ignore my message. I rang him back, muttered something about imminent vomit, told him it was a false alarm and hung up.

At this point in my morning, I could really have done with a nice cup of tea. Cursing Paul for using the last tea bag, I made another coffee to keep my caffeine levels topped up. It really wasn't Paul's fault, but it felt good to blame someone. He was only a man after all, and wouldn't have thought to check the cupboard for a new box of tea bags, let alone re-fill the empty jar. Had he done so, he might've had the presence of mind to leave his used bag for me. (No, I'm not a fan of sloppy seconds, but needs must and all that.) Poor Paul, he really couldn't win with me. He hadn't made me my usual cuppa before heading out the door at 7 a.m. for the hour long drive to work, because he thought I could do with a lie-in after the bad night with Tom. He always had the best of intentions, but somehow he always got it wrong. Didn't stand a chance really, poor sod. Obviously, it was really my fault that there was no replacement pack of tea bags in the larder, but I was feeling bad enough already without admitting that.

After I had hung up the second lot of washing, I sat down to cuddle Tom. Mercifully, he dozed off within minutes and I snuck off to the computer to see if anyone was available to chat on Facebook. At the very least I could update my status to something provocative in the hope of triggering a discussion. Sadly, everyone else seemed to have got a life and I resorted to searching for old friends from school. Even ones I never really liked. Lucy, you're a sad cow. When a search for 'Sally Smith' produced thousands of results, I gave up and, remembering the cascade of sick in Tom's bedroom, I set off upstairs once more.

Cleaning up sick, be it human or animal, is never a pleasant experience. It is, however, much worse without rubber gloves. I couldn't find any rubber gloves (never been a big fan of the things) so I had to undertake the evil task with naked hands. When I had finished I gave my hands a thorough wash using a new soap I'd just opened in the bathroom. Said soap promised to be 'Anti-bacterial' with the scent of orange zest, and would leave my hands feeling 'fresh, clean and soft'. Fresh my arse.

They should have stated, 'Will leave your hands feeling soft, clean and smelling of washing that was put away damp'. I think I preferred the combined aroma of sick and Zoflora.

With the carpets now smelling fresher than my hands, I wondered if today would be the day that drove me to drink? My night out with Jess had proven that I could drink alcohol without too many adverse effects. Maybe the occasional glass of wine in the evening was just what I needed to relax and unwind. I knew lots of other parents who resorted to a nice glass of red when the kids were in bed, so there must be something in it. Yeah, alcohol, stupid. I knew that Paul would love someone to share a bottle of wine with. (Not me if I didn't start being a bit nicer to him.) I know there were occasions when he would have liked a drink or two after a long day in the office, but he didn't like to open a bottle just for him. I still wasn't convinced that alcohol was the answer at this point, as I could see that a glass or two could easily become a bottle or two, and before I knew it I'd be hiding bottles of cheap vodka in the cupboard under the sink. I assumed this was a good hiding place for cheap vodka as I was sure it had multiple cleaning uses and its presence could therefore be explained as such.

Deciding that, for now, alcohol wasn't the answer to my problems, I ate three chocolate chip brioches. And then I felt even more miserable. So I toasted some syrup pancakes and slathered them with butter. And then of course I felt even more fed up. Literally. I vowed that tomorrow I would get back to healthy eating. (Knowing full well that tomorrow never comes, especially with the winter nights drawing in and the SAD season upon us.) Bemoaning my lack of willpower, I was reminded of something a very skinny super model once said:

'Nothing tastes as good as skinny feels.' Even though I knew I was much happier when slim, I still couldn't get this adage to work for me. Chocolate chip brioches and syrup pancakes slathered in butter taste bloody fantastic.

Telling myself that all I could do for now was take one day at a time (sounds like something they might tell you at Alcoholics Anonymous), I resigned myself to the inevitable crapness of this particular day and went to check on Tom. Make that inevitable sickness…

40

Balls to Christmas

It was the first week of December, three months had passed since my surgery, along with a pretty much unmarked forty-fourth birthday, and my breasts were starting to look slightly less repulsive. Even the dog ear seemed to have settled down a bit (more of a King Charles than a Springer spaniel now) and I was more hopeful of not needing an additional nip and tuck; unless they were prepared to throw in a bit of liposuction at the same time. Admittedly Simon's nipple was never going to be the same size as Anita's, but I could live with that. What I couldn't live without was cleavage. I guess I'd taken my cleavage for granted when I had it. Now I mourned its loss, and wondered if I'd ever get it back. My friends tried to reassure me that I just needed the right bra, so I ordered one which promised 'maximum enhancement'. The only thing it enhanced when I put it on was my misery. I told myself it was still early days as I dejectedly put my sports bra back on and tossed the (un)enhancer bra into the back of a drawer from where it couldn't mock me.

My undies drawer was still full of my old bras as I hadn't been able to bring myself to throw them away. Apparently, I'm no better at letting go of old lingerie than I am old boyfriends. I wondered briefly (ha ha) what a psychologist would make of me, and decided that I really ought to ditch the huge brassieres.

I don't know why I found it so hard to get rid of them. Apart from the fact that they'd cost a hell of a lot of money and it seemed a big waste. Big being the operative word.

I had vowed to have a big bra-burning ceremony-thing, but that idea had fizzled out. Maybe I could make hammocks out of them? Or send them to Oxfam to be used as housing in the third world? In the end, I just bundled them up in a black sack (bar one which I kept for posterity) and put them out for the dustmen. Well, not *for* the dustmen exactly, that would be an interesting Christmas bonus, but you know what I mean. Oh dear. I've got that picture in my head now and it's not pretty.

In an attempt to take my mind off my lack of cleavage, I turned my attention to Christmas.

Personally I find Christmas rather over-rated. Not to the extent that I refuse to buy presents and I go round muttering 'Bah, humbug' under my breath, but I do find it a bit of an anti-climax. You spend ages getting ready for it, shopping and planning, writing cards, putting decorations up – the list is endless – and then it's all over in a flash. Then comes all the un-decorating and clearing up afterwards. I'd rather spend the money, and the time, on a nice holiday somewhere warm. Oh dear, I do sound rather scrooge-like don't I? And of course, there's Tom to consider. Every child deserves the traditional family Christmas don't they? I just thought it would be nice to try the traditional Australian family Christmas for a change, and spend the holiday season on the beach, bunging prawns on the barbie, with not an overcooked sprout in sight.

I don't know when I turned into such a miserable old boot. I can remember a time (just) when I used to love thinking up the perfect presents for all my family and friends. Something personal and fitting, which showed how well I knew them and that I cared enough to really put some thought into their gift. Now it was a case of going into as few shops as possible, using very little imagination and feeling relieved when there was something vaguely appropriate to wrap for everyone on my list. Most of these presents would probably end up being donated as raffle prizes at the next village fete, or put in a cupboard and forgotten about. It would serve me right if I was given some of them back next Christmas. I had even resorted to online shopping for some things, which was the ultimate in laziness and can't-be-bothered-ness. What had happened to make me such a Christmas cynic?

I pondered this question as I decorated the artificial tree. Yes, you heard me, artificial tree. I wondered if this was part of the problem. Christmas had become unnatural, imitation, and the tree was a symbol of this. In years gone by I'd always insisted on a real tree and had resisted when others suggested an artificial one would be more practical. When had Christmas become about practicality? Surely hoovering up the dropped needles couldn't have been that much of a chore? Maybe it had been. I tried to remember when and why the change to a fake tree had taken place.

Then in a flash (probably a bulb blowing on the set of lights I was draping around the tree) it all came flooding back. That bloody dog. Pippin had been the reason we abandoned real trees. Every time he brushed past the tree he caused a flurry of needles to drop on both him and the carpet. And those sharp little pine needles irritated his skin and got in his feet and caused no end of misery. And potential vet bills. So, the real tree had to go. Of course, since then Pippin had gone too, but by then the fake tree had become established.

With a sigh, for the loss of Pippin and the real trees, I continued hanging assorted red and gold baubles from the imitation tree branches. That's when I realised I should've put the tinsel on first. Oops. Oh well, I'll pretend it was a deliberate mistake and go for the less is more option. By the time I'd finished, the tree looked surprisingly tasteful. More by accident than design I have to say. Feeling a little better about life, and Christmas, I decided to decorate Tom's playroom as an after-school surprise. I found a whole load of shiny silver streamers to suspend from the walls and ceiling. Armed with a new packet of Blu-tack (I didn't want to use drawing pins in what was a newly decorated room), I attempted to festoon the room in glittery gorgeousness. Unfortunately, as fast as I stuck one end of the garland, another would come unstuck and fall to the floor.

I tried to stay calm about the whole thing, but was rapidly getting more wound up than the sets of lights I'd untangled earlier. I was close to ripping the whole lot down and chucking it in the bin, but then thought of Tom's delighted face when he saw my handiwork and vowed to have one more go. Suffice to say there is now more Blu-tack on my playroom ceiling than in the Blu-tack factory.

'Bah bloody humbug,' I muttered to myself as I tidied up the mess I had made in my attempts to make the house look festive. Frankly, if Saint Nick himself had popped his head down the chimney at that moment I may just have punched his lights out. Right on cue, the lights on the tree went out. 'Bloody buggering bummocks,' I snarled as I threw down a box of assorted balls and stormed from the room.

As I stood in the kitchen, staring out of the window while I waited for the coffee machine to do its thing, I wondered again what had turned me into Dr. Seuss's Christmas-hating 'Grinch'. I had read the story to Tom a hundred times and could recite most of it from memory:

'*The Grinch hated Christmas! The whole Christmas season!*
Now, please don't ask why. No one quite knows the reason.
It could be his head wasn't screwed on just right.
It could be, perhaps, that his shoes were too tight.
But I think that the most likely reason of all
May have been that his heart was two sizes too small.'

It was certainly true that I had the odd screw loose, but I didn't think that was the reason; it definitely couldn't be my shoes as I always opted for comfort over style these days. Which left only one possible conclusion: my heart had shrunk. Well, unless the size of my heart was in direct proportion to my bust size, I didn't think my op could be to blame. I tried to think back to my last really happy Christmas, and the image that kept coming back to me was the year that Dan had bought me a ring. With a sigh, I wondered if I would ever get over him?

41

Getting things off my chest

I felt like crying. Or screaming. Or both. I wouldn't though because I was too bloody knackered from lack of sleep. It had been over three months since my op and Paul, my saintly oh-so-patient husband, had decided that I should be back in the marital bed. Bugger. I'd enjoyed my nun-like existence in the spare room with just an occasional cat for company. Paul, however, had not being getting any satisfaction from his none-like one, with just an occasional cat or small son for company. To be frank, I was dreading sharing a bed again. I knew full well that I'd never get a good night's sleep and just the thought of it was tiring. You can take that 'it' to mean anything you like.

I was currently still wearing my sports bra at night, after liberally rubbing in scar-reducing oil or whatever suitable mois-turiser was to hand. For weeks I could hardly stand to touch my Frankenstein breasts, but it was now getting less stom-ach-turning. Paul had offered to undertake this unpleasant task for me, for purely selfless reasons naturally, but the prospect of letting him near my breasts was still cringe-making. And I'm pretty sure it wasn't rescue-oil he planned to use either. On a positive note, my boobs were starting to take shape. That is to say, a shape that was appropriate and would fit in a bra. Just the one bra mind. Most still did nothing at all for me. I kept telling myself it was early days and I was trying to be patient, but patience is not one of my virtues. For Paul's sake I hoped he didn't buy me a load of gorgeous bras for Christmas. I may just have strangled him with one of them.

Well, that was Christmas over for another year. Thank God. Let's hope the New Year was a big improvement on the old one. To be honest, at the moment I'd be grateful for a small one. Improvement that is. I still hadn't managed to kick the miserable old boot that was me into touch and had no idea of how to perk myself up. Plastic surgery certainly wasn't going to work this time I sighed as I tucked into another box of chocolates left over from Christmas. Although, if I carried on eating like I had been all winter, liposuction and a tummy tuck would be required. I found it harder than ever to eat sensibly during the winter months. I told myself it was an instinctual thing, to put on extra blubber to keep warm through the freezing days and nights. Hmm. This may have been true before the days of central heating, but I would be hard pushed to use it as a justification for eating like a pig when the radiators were on constantly and the house was positively toasty. Now there's a thought... toast with enough butter spread on it to leave teeth marks when you bit into it. Four slices should do for now.

Post-toast and I was feeling guilty about comfort eating. Again. Maybe some chocolate would cheer me up. Nope. Just felt more guilty now. I consider myself a reasonably intelligent woman and I know all about healthy eating and nutrition. In other words I know what's good for me. And I love being slim. I'm happier when I'm slim. So why the hell was I constantly shovelling junk into my mouth, piling on the weight and feeling more miserable by the day? Did I simply lack will power?

Or was there a deeper, underlying reason for my over-eating? Answers on a postcard please, because I sure as hell didn't know.

My mood was not improved as I followed the trail of destruction left by the male members of the family around the house. I was seriously considering writing a book of amazing facts for boys of all ages, to include the following astonishing truths:

Doors and drawers don't only open. They shut too. Astounding, I know.

Lights turn off as well as on. It's a miracle.

Dirty washing doesn't pick itself up off the floor. Ditto dirty dishes. There are no fairies.

If you get something out it is possible to put it away again when you have finished with it. Nothing bad will happen to you. Promise.

You only need the television on in the room you're actually in. Ditto PlayStation, Xbox, Wii, PC, etc.

It is not OK to leave one sheet of paper on the loo roll just so you don't have to get a new one.

If, by some miracle, you do change the loo roll, it is quite safe to put the old one in the bin. Go the extra mile, boys.

When removing socks, it is not compulsory to hurl them to the four corners of the room. (Honestly I find them on top of the wardrobes sometimes.)

I could go on ad infinitum. It wasn't as though I was asking them to multi-task or something. These were things which could be done in sequence. I realised men had their limits after all, and I didn't think I was being unreasonable. And then there was the whole issue of putting the toilet seat down after they've used the loo. When I first tried to get Paul to put the loo seat down he looked completely mystified. He didn't see why he should put the seat down for me as I didn't lift it up for him. I felt like screaming at him that it wasn't about being polite, but about keeping in any unpleasant sights and smells. He thought I meant just the bit of the loo ladies sit on, when of course I meant the lid bit. I might as well have been explaining nuclear physics. In Mandarin. To a guinea-pig. I gave up in the end. After all, I had to go up to the bathroom after him to turn the light off, so I might as well do the lid while I was there.

Now, it seemed, Tom was following in his father's footsteps and I despaired at ever getting him fully house-trained. Come back Pippin, all was forgiven. Not only did Tom leave the lid up and the light on, but he didn't bother to flush either. Or wipe his bottom. No matter how many times I reminded him, he still seemed unable to comply with this simple instruction. He also lied about washing his hands no matter how often I tried to scare him about toilet germs making him ill. I'd started to think these behaviours must be genetic and that this was a battle I would never win until some sort of gene therapy became available.

By the time I'd been round the house closing all the cupboards and drawers, picking up and putting away everything they'd left out, turning off everything they weren't using, there was no time to actually do anything else. I realised that these things were minor and probably not grounds for divorce, but the cumulative effect was considerable and contributed to the anti-men feelings festering in my brain. And other places. It's just a shame I didn't fancy women as lesbianism would otherwise be hugely appealing.

Every now and again, Paul surprised me by getting some-thing right. I'd find he had picked up the bath mat to stop it from getting mildewed underneath. Woo hoo! I was making progress at last. Wrong. It was just a blip. The exception that proved the rule I sighed as I lifted the bath mat yet again.

I found myself muttering under my breath a lot. And calling Paul names behind his back. And I don't mean 'Darling'. I didn't much like the person I'd become: a grumpy old woman who was never satisfied. I knew I was making Paul unhappy too; he felt that he could never do anything right (well he'd got a point I thought to myself) and I knew full well that my constant criticism was emasculating him. It was rapidly reaching a point whereby he no longer felt like trying as he was guaranteed to fail in my eyes. I wasn't sure if I was the rock or the hard place, but Paul was definitely stuck.

Clearly drastic action was needed, so I texted the other mums and suggested a coffee morning as soon as possible. Charlie, Zoe, Sarah and Claire were only too happy to oblige and we arranged to meet at Sarah's after school drop-off the following day. I got the impression that we were are all suffering from a combination of seasonal depression and a nasty bout of misan-dry. Maybe misandry is too strong a word: we didn't hate all men, just the ones we were married to. I made a mental note to buy some chocolate biscuits to take with me and looked forward to being able to get everything off my chest (what was left of it) very soon.

42

a sad state of affairs

By five past nine the next morning, we were all ensconced in Sarah's lounge with coffee and choccie biccies, preparing to try and out-do each other with stories of how annoying our husbands were. Claire got in first, mainly because she was always on a diet and therefore not stuffing her face with biscuits. To be honest, Claire didn't have that much to complain about with her husband. He did most of the housework, almost all the cooking and shared the school runs. Not only that, but he was a demon decorator and a great gardener. We had suggested that she hire him out to assist us more needy women around the house, but to no avail.

Charlie went next. She was a one biscuit kind of a woman. Her turn didn't take long either as she'd only recently moved in with her new boyfriend and hadn't quite lost the honeymoon glow. Her moans consisted mainly of smelly rugby kit festering in a sports bag and generally adjusting to sharing a house with someone after being on her own for five years. Make the most of it Charlie, I thought to myself, as it may soon reach the stage where you resent everything he says and everything he does; when the sound of him chewing made you want to reach for the carving knife and you had permanent teeth marks in your tongue from constantly biting it to stop yourself from saying something you might regret. Or not.

By now, I was on my third extra-thick chocolate biscuit and happy to listen as Sarah bemoaned her (c)lot in life. Sarah's husband, Gary, was a lot like Paul, so I empathised particularly with her and always felt a great sisterly solidarity as she recounted Gary's latest faux pas. Today she was particularly pissed off with him and said she could understand why so many women in their forties became lesbians. Everyone except me recoiled slightly and Sarah and I looked at each other and laughed. I suggested some sort of communal living as a compromise. All us women and children shared one big house, with men welcome by invitation only.

'Imagine,' I said, 'no wet towels on the bed, no shaving stubble left in the bathroom sink, no dirty underwear dumped on the bedroom floor... the list is endless.'

'It does sound good,' admitted Sarah with a sigh. 'No belching, scratching and picking. And no snoring. Just imagine getting a good night's sleep. Every night. Bliss.'

'Men really are disgusting creatures aren't they?' Sarah again. Clearly she and I were singing off the same hymn sheet here. And it wasn't 'All Things Bright and Beautiful'.

'And then they have the audacity to wonder why we don't want to have sex with them!' I announced forcefully.

'I know,' Sarah rejoined.

At this point I noticed that Zoe, Claire and Charlie had gone rather quiet. Clearly they still fancied their men. Well hoo-bloody-ray for them, I thought. I was feeling a little mutinous by now. Clearly Sarah was still with me as she bemoaned the fact that she and Gary had a night in a hotel coming up and that he would expect sex. We mourned the fact that a night away in a hotel would once have had us chomping at the bit with anticipation. Now it was more of a punishment, something to be endured rather than enjoyed. This was a very sad state of affairs. Maybe that was the answer. Have an affair. Feeling reckless, I opened up a discussion on the merits of affairs, mistresses and swinging. Having bugger all personal experience to draw on wasn't going to stop me. I'd read enough Jilly Cooper novels and seen enough films on the subject to have an opinion.

'I did suggest to Paul that he get a mistress,' I announced as my opening gambit, trying to keep a straight face as I said it. 'Apart from me not wanting to have sex with him, we get on OK most of the time. We could just be companions and parents. But the whole sex thing (or lack thereof) screws everything up (or not). I feel guilty about not wanting sex, Paul feels frustrated and takes it personally and the knock on effect is a miserable household. He didn't like the idea though – says he only wants me. Selfish bastard. One little thing I ask him to do…'

I sneaked a look at Sarah, who was stifling a giggle, and gave her a sly grin. She appeared to be the only one in the room who realised I was joking (in the main).

'Well, if he won't have an affair, maybe you should Lucy. They do say that the more sex you have, the more you want. It's the whole use it or lose it thing. Maybe another man could stoke your fire and you'd get your libido back on track.'

'Humph,' I grunted, unconvinced. 'These embers are barely glowing; it would take one hell of a fire-lighter to produce a flame. Besides, I really don't fancy stripping off in front of another man with all these newly acquired scars. I don't think my patchwork boobs would be much of a turn on. Add them to my caesarean scar and I look rather like something Dr. Frankenstein might have made. And don't get me started on my saggy belly and cellulite.'

'Men don't even see that stuff,' Sarah assured me. 'Thankfully, men see us through rose-tinted spectacles. It's like when they breathe in before they stand in front of the mirror: they only see what they want to see. You've got nothing to worry about.'

'But what about the guilt?' I asked as I helped myself to another guilt-inducing biscuit.

'Think of it as a means to an end. If having sex with another man gets your marriage back on track, then everyone's a winner. Imagine it as being no different to taking Viagra, and that it's been prescribed by your GP,' Sarah giggled.

'But where on earth would I go to collect my "prescription"? In the past I've always met men through my job. Now I'm a housewife, the only men I see on a regular basis are the postman and Tom's teacher. The postman is so not my type (or anybody else's I shouldn't think) and Mr. Goodyear looks about fourteen.'

'What about exes?' suggested Sarah. 'Any exes still on the scene who might be up for it?'

This was dangerous ground. Sarah had unwittingly tapped into a major weakness: my inability to let go of the past. Feeling suddenly vulnerable, I pooh-poohed the idea with a scathing 'Oh please, they're exes for a reason', and then rapidly changed the subject. To swinging.

By this time, the others had started to realise that Sarah and I were just messing about and they joined in with a very giggly conversation about throwing car keys into a bowl and subsequently getting intimately acquainted with the owner of one particular set of keys. How would we go about choosing by key alone? After all, a man's choice of car could say a lot about him. A flashy sports car might indicate mid-life crisis or suggest he was not so well-endowed in the trouser department. Even choosing a Jaguar or BMW driver was a gamble as they could range from fat sweaty businessman to suave sophisticated playboy. It was a minefield.

'What about a Volvo driver?' Claire asked.

'Hmm. Safety conscious. He'd probably carry a condom,' laughed Charlie.

They were really getting into the swing of things now.

'Then there are the boy racers who have a souped-up Vauxhall Nova and a boot full of stereo equipment. Or worse still, the ones who carry Ferrari keyrings but really drive clapped out old bangers with bumper stickers saying 'my other car's a Ferrari'', said Zoe.

We eventually came to the conclusion that choosing by car was largely unsound and that we should perhaps go for the guy who came on his bike. At least he'd be fit.

As I drove home from Sarah's, in my low-slung sporty looking silver car which could be considered a sign of a mid-life crisis, I thought back to her comment about exes. Dan had been on my mind a lot since I'd found out about his split from Freya. I wondered if he ever thought about me and what might have been. Mentally giving myself a kick up the backside that of course he didn't or he wouldn't have married Freya in the first place, I pushed him to the back of my mind, to the area of my brain reserved for exes. It was a little overcrowded in there, but I just couldn't quite let any of them move out. If I could charge them rent I'd be a rich woman.

Hard as I tried to keep Dan out of my thoughts, he was constantly at the forefront of my mind. Pushing him away was like trying to stop the tide from turning. I tried to remember all the bad things about the relationship and the fact that I had been unhappy for quite a while when we split up. We'd never have worked, I insisted to myself, but that didn't stop me from remembering how he'd made me feel in the beginning. In my heart of hearts I knew that Dan wasn't the answer. The trouble was, with him in my head I couldn't even remember what the question was.

Later that night, after Tom had gone to bed (if not to sleep) I told Paul about my natter with the girls and we laughed at the whole notion of swinging. We both knew that neither of us would ever be up for it. I laughed even more when I came back downstairs after taking Tom up a drink and saw a bowl of keys on the coffee table. I really wasn't in the mood, but I still felt mean as I fished out my own keys and took myself off to the spare room…

43

The bald truth

I was temporarily distracted from thoughts of my ailing marriage after school the following day.

Tom had nits. Correction, Tom had nit. Make that did have nit as I have removed the offending wee beastie. I have to admit to being a little confused about the whole nit thing actually. Am I right in thinking that the little bug things are head lice and that their eggs are called nits? In which case, Tom had head louse. I didn't find any eggs, so could I say with a degree of truth that Tom didn't have nits? I wondered if it would be OK to tell Tom not to mention it to anyone? Not lie exactly, but just omit to mention it. Lying by omission's not really so bad is it? I decided to play it by ear with the other mums. That is where I found the little sucker after all. Lucy, you could justify absolutely anything if you tried hard enough.

Following that fateful day, I religiously combed through Tom's hair with the nit comb while he was in the bath. I was relieved not to find anymore nits or creepy crawlies thereafter, but vowed to keep a close eye on things. To be on the safe side I also used the nit comb on myself. It didn't remove any nits, just a hell of a lot of hair. I hoped I wouldn't have to use it too often as I would end up bald. Although at least if I was bald I couldn't get head lice I mused; they'd have nothing to cling on to. Combing my own quite long hair made me feel a pang of sympathy for mums with daughters. I could now understand why Claire lost the plot whenever her little girl came out of school with her hair out of its pony tail. When modern day fairy tales came to be written, Rapunzel wouldn't be letting down her hair for the witch to ascend to her tower room. No, Britney Chantelle would be removing her scrunchie and inviting the head lice to climb the staircase of her hair to her tower block room 'coz the lift's broken. And smells of piss.

I kept the head louse discovery under my hat for a few weeks, until one day I was standing in the playground with Zoe and Claire, waiting for school to finish, and somehow the subject came up. How relieved was I when they both admitted to finding lice on their two. We'd obviously all been too ashamed to say anything. What a relief that we were all in the same boat.

This admission threw up another thorny issue. How could we slag off the itchy head brigade now? It didn't take long to resolve this problem. Obviously head lice were not choosy and even the nicest children from the nicest of homes could catch head lice (from the not-so-nice children from the not-so-nice homes). So, the fault clearly lay with the parents who didn't take action to rid their children of the problem. Despite numerous letters from the school explaining how to de-lice your children and that not to do so is practically child abuse, these parents did nothing. Shocking. Super. We could still take the moral high (play)ground.

While I'm in confessional mode, I have also to admit that I bought a moisturiser with a hint of foundation yesterday. Now I know this isn't the same as getting up at 5 a.m. to plaster on my face before appearing in public, but was it the start of a slippery slope? Before you knew it, I'd be applying mascara. Then it'd be a little bit of gloss on my lips. Maybe a touch of bronzer. Where would it end? I'd also resorted to having a few highlights in my hair to disguise the first greys that were appearing. Call it vanity if you like. I do. I was forty four years old, but didn't want to look it. Until now, people have always said I don't look my age. (I'm assuming they meant I looked younger than my years.) Well, now I really didn't want to look my age. I didn't want people to start saying that I looked good, and then qualifying it with 'for your age'.

When my eye cream ran out today, I thought about doing the same thing. Screaming. It had been one of those weeks. Instead, I added eye cream to the shopping list and headed for the supermarket. As they didn't stock my usual brand, I had to choose from the multitude of others available. Somehow I ended up buying the one with a 'hint of concealer' in it. I didn't even have to ponder over which shade to choose (as I had with the moisturiser); this amazing under-eye cream promised 'skin-adaptive colour'. While feeling a little sceptical about the truth of this miraculous promise, the hefty price tag convinced me it must be true and I popped the miniscule tube in my trolley, hoping it wouldn't disappear through the holes and roll under the counter in the fruit and veg aisle. (I'd had previous experience of this sort of thing when Tom had insisted on taking a toy into the shop with him, and I really didn't fancy getting down on my hands and knees next to the bananas.)

While I was in the vicinity of make-up, I had a quick browse along the shelves, but I didn't spot any chap sticks with a hint of lipstick, or an eye lash brush with a hint of mascara. I really wasn't ready to start wearing make-up every day. Paul would probably think I was having an affair. (Was I thinking about having an affair…?) Leaving the make-up stands I headed for deodorants; mine really wasn't cutting the mustard anymore (whatever that means) and it was time to try a different one. Blimey, Lucy, I thought to myself, you really live life on the edge. Whatever next? Aquafresh instead of Colgate, perhaps? Persil instead of Ariel? Anything was possible while I was feeling so reckless. Maybe I'd streak round PJ's Funhouse, which was where Tom and I were headed after school.

There were the usual suspects at PJ's that afternoon, and we somehow got onto the subject of exes: boyfriends, husbands, one-night stands and the like. Or the don't like - that's why they were exes. I had my own theory on why I chose the men I did, so I was curious to find out what the others thought. My hypothesis was that I jumped from one extreme to the other: from Mr. Tidy to Mr. Messy, or from Mr. A-Bit-Too-Posh to Mr. A-Little-Bit-of-Rough and so on.

I had concluded long ago that this was not the best way to choose a potential life partner, but it made no difference. I was repelled so forcefully from the things which I disliked about a man, that I was thrust too far in the opposite direction. Rather like the ball in a pin-ball machine. Sure enough, in no time at all, I'd realise the error of my ways and start looking for someone who was the polar opposite of my current man to rebound onto. I don't think it was ever a conscious decision but it was always a recipe for disaster. I just couldn't seem to find any middle ground to settle on.

Zoe admitted she too had gone to extremes: her first husband had been a bit of a wimp and her current partner was the ultimate man's man, a butch builder. Claire said that she was just so flattered when anyone asked her out, that she always said yes, and then worried about how to dump them at a later date. Sarah just sighed and said that she'd been with Gary for so long she couldn't remember any previous boyfriends.

'It's a shame I can't off-load a few of mine onto you,' I said. 'Might clear some space in my brain for something a bit more useful. If only I could spring clean my head at the same time as I spring clean the house,' I mused.

The only flaw I could see in this plan was the fact that I didn't actually spring clean the house. But I thought about it. And it was the thought that counted. I am a very thoughtful person I'll have you know. Just slightly lacking in whatever it is that turns thoughts into actions.

Naturally, talking about our exes led on to us talking about our potential-exes.

'Have you noticed,' chimed in Charlie, who'd been rather quiet until now, 'that all your blokes are virtually bald?'

'Unlike yours,' chipped Sarah, 'who has a full head of hair as well as being young, tall and handsome.'

'It's true though,' said Claire, whose husband was the baldest of the lot. 'They are all follically challenged.'

There followed an analysis of why four women of a certain age, yet to have children, were attracted to this particular look. Could it really come down to the theory that bald men were more virile? Well, we all now had at least one child each from our baldies, so maybe there was something in this.

'Of course the other old wives' tale associated with baldness, is that it's caused by too much masturbation.' I pointed out.

'You know, the hair is lost off the head and grows on the man's palms instead.'

'So, basically,' said Sarah, 'they're all just a bunch of wankers?'

'A good point well made. Anyone for frothy coffee?'

44

Curtains for Louie?

Louie had also been doing his bit to keep me from brooding about my relationship with Paul. Unfortunately, it would appear that Louie was reverting to his alter ego, and Le Wee had been putting in some unwelcome appearances. Make that a-pee-rances. Maybe he was sensitive to the tension between me and Paul, I wondered idly. And if the pets were picking up on the atmosphere, maybe Tom was too? I sincerely hoped he wasn't about to start acting up in the toilet department.

As usual, his favourite spot was the lounge curtains. (Louie's, not Tom's. Tom usually managed to pee in the vicinity of the toilet, even if his aim wasn't always spot on.) Naturally, the curtains were labelled 'Dry Clean Only' and I had thus far resisted bunging this particular pair in the washing machine. However, I really couldn't face the prospect of hand-washing the affected patch and was certainly not forking out to have them dry-cleaned. So, into the washing machine the curtain went, on a cool gentle cycle which could surely do no harm. Certainly the curtain looked fine when I hung it up to dry. Not so fine when I hung it back up in the lounge next to its opposite number and found that it was now a couple of inches shorter. Great. I needn't have worried though. It wasn't long before Louie obliged by peeing up the other curtain and I gave it the same treatment. Thankfully, it shrank pretty much the same amount. The only problem I foresaw was that sooner or later I would have to get a smaller window.

45

I'm snow angel

It was 4 a.m. and I was sitting on the sofa with a cup of tea and a book. Insomnia had struck again. Unfortunately, it hadn't knocked me out. I wasn't actually reading the book, which was titled, rather ironically, *Wake Up to Insomnia*. I'd tried but had to keep re-reading the same sentence and still couldn't take it in. I picked up the other book I'd bought recently, in a moment of desperation, *Put the Magic Back in Your Marriage*, turned it over and skimmed the blurb on the back cover. The author promised to show me 'how to rediscover the magical attraction' that first drew me and Paul together, and 'reignite the embers' of our love. I chucked the book back on the coffee table with a sigh. Even David Copperfield would be hard pressed to put any magic back in my marriage.

I could hear rain on the windows and it was a surprisingly welcome sound after days of heavy snow which had caused havoc on the roads. Tom had missed a couple of days of school much to his delight. I can't say the feeling was mutual. When I did sleep, everything in my dreams was now made from Lego bricks and if I knelt or stood on another of the sodding things I'd scream. I had tried to persuade Tom to go sledging, but he refused.

He was always so afraid of trying anything new. I think he might choose a career in Health and Safety when he's older.

You could practically see him doing a mental risk assessment when faced with something untried. I even made a virtual Winter Olympics using all the white bits of Lego, and made a red sledge like Tom's with a little Lego man on. All to no avail. (I don't think my cause was helped when said little Lego man's head came off after a nasty fall.) Tom was immoveable however, and no amount of cajoling or bribery worked. He didn't care that all his friends would be sledging at every available opportunity. I gave up when he turned on the waterworks and switched on the television, only to catch a snippet of news saying that a teenage girl had died in a freak sledging accident.

A couple of days later, Paul and I decided to have another go at persuading Tom to give sledging a try. We really thought he was missing out, and who knew when we might have this amount of snow again? Besides, he'd asked for a sledge so he could ruddy well use it. I think we finally talked him into it at three pounds fifty. Needless to say, a short time later, Tom was whizzing down the hill shouting 'This is awesome!' and asking why we hadn't been sledging before. Aaaggghhh!

So, we did get some enjoyment from the snow and I have a collection of lovely photos of Tom making snow angels and building a snowman. It was a pretty pathetic snowman admittedly. We never seemed to manage one of those brilliant snow creations which always get shown on the local news. Just one of the many ways in which I am a failure as a parent, I sighed.

It was with an even bigger sigh that I remembered Paul's car. We were waiting to hear if it was going to be written off after he slid into the central reservation on the dual carriageway during the worst of the weather. He was really cross with himself and I had tried to make him feel better by saying things like: 'It could have been worse,' and 'at least you're OK'. I'm not sure which was the most dented: Paul's car or his pride. Thank God there wasn't a £400 excess on his pride too.

I had such mixed feelings about snow now. Being a grown-up really sucked sometimes. I still got excited when it snowed hard. I still thought it was incredibly beautiful and loved how the world looked under a blanket of snow. But, at the same time, it had become inconvenient and expensive. Suddenly all the things we normally took for granted, like getting to the shops or taking the kids to school, became fraught with difficulty and danger. I was in mourning for the loss of my childhood; that carefree time when all the snow meant was endless fun and games. Oh the innocence of youth. We don't appreciate it when we've got it though do we? And now I'm old(er) and wise(r) (OK, so wiser's pushing it), and so very cynical. I reckon if I tried to make a snow angel it would have horns.

Being a parent changed how you viewed the world too didn't it? I'm sure as a girl I used to eat snow by the glove-ful, but now I found myself advising Tom not to eat the snow (yellow or otherwise). What was that all about? I hadn't heard them talking about acid-rain on the news of late, let alone acid-snow. I didn't think eating snow ever did me any harm, so why was I so uptight about my own child doing it? Surely, he had the same right to experience the things which I experienced as a child? (Yeah, let him have braces and a lisp I thought.) I did so hate double standards but I seemed to have become the queen of them. I resolved to try to change my behaviour but I knew it was a battle I probably wouldn't win. I thought maybe something happened to a woman after she'd had a baby. She turned into her mother.

So, now it was raining and the beautiful white snow was turning to grey slush. And I was pleased. Being stuck at home with an over-excited six-year-old and a pissed off husband who'd smashed up his car was no fun. Could be worse though I suppose: could be the other way around. I never thought I'd say this, but the snow had become a pain in the bum. Speaking of which... I had been soooooooooo constipated lately!

I knew it was largely my own fault. My crappy diet (oh the irony) and lack of exercise were the likely culprits, but I was fast becoming reliant on laxatives and something had got to give. Apparently not my bowel it seemed. I was sitting on the sofa, watching daytime television and swilling down another glass of Movicol followed by a coffee chaser, when a *Diet Doctor* programme came on. (Another of those 'it's a sign' moments by which I lived my life a lot of the time.)

Anyway, I decided watching it was a good excuse to avoid doing any housework for a bit longer and settled back with a packet of chocolate biscuits, hoping for some sort of Eureka moment to strike. Half-an-hour later and I was Googling colonic irrigation. Before I chickened out, I'd made an appointment at a clinic which looked reputable and whose practices sounded hygienic, to have something called 'colonic hydrotherapy' which I assumed was the less agricultural sounding name for the procedure. I knew Paul would laugh at me, but desperate times and all that. Anyway, he ought to be the one with a problem – he was even unhealthier than me and yet I could set my watch by his bowel movements which were as hideously regular as they were pungent. Even Tom, who lived on cheese and chocolate, pooed without problem. Life could be so unfair.

I have to say that on the way to the clinic I was buttock-clench-ingly nervous. (I think my bum knew what was coming – and going hopefully – and was trying to block the way, but I'd had enough of blockages and would have to show it who was boss.) The sat nav didn't fail me (damn) and soon I was pulling up outside the clinic. I breathed a sigh of relief when there wasn't a DIY shop or a plumber's anywhere to be seen. It just looked like a beauty salon or hairdresser's shop front, and there wasn't a big arrow and a sign saying 'step inside and have a hose shoved up yer bum'.

I was greeted by a pleasant, middle-aged woman who told me to come in and relax. I assumed she was joking, but took a seat on a comfortable-looking leather sofa. I wondered idly if they had leather to make cleaning any nasty accidents up easier. I knew from my experiences with Tom just how difficult poo stains could be.

After the necessary forms were filled out, Sue-rhymes-with-poo, the therapist, explained the procedure. I just nodded and giggled nervously. I guess we never really grow out of being embarrassed by our private bits and bodily functions. Tom and his friends found anything to do with bottoms and willies terribly funny, but they were only six. I told myself that having been through labour and having had my nipples removed, I could handle a colonic.

It wasn't the most pleasant experience of my life, but it wasn't particularly unpleasant either. Since I had it done I have felt better than I have in ages; fewer headaches, more energy and generally feeling relieved. Paul says I'm just relieved that it's over. I knew I was nice and clean now and no longer full of toxic nasties. No more eating processed food and junk for me,

I resolved. From now on I would only eat things grown on a plant, not those made in a plant.

Before my good intentions could wither, I set off to buy a whole host of vegetables to make a meat-free, home-made lasagne. I knew I had my work cut out trying to convert Paul to healthy eating, but I was going to try. Normally, just the mention of an aubergine had him pulling faces similar to those made by Tom when I tried to get him to eat sprouts. Normally, if I had a veggie meal, Paul would have a slab of meat on the side. He was old-fashioned in his eating habits and believed that a meal without meat was not a meal. Don't get me wrong, I didn't think I could ever give up meat altogether, but I did enjoy meat-free meals now and again. For Paul, I think it was a bit like enforced celibacy – not something he'd ever choose for himself.

As we sat down to dinner that night, I could tell that Paul was less than enthusiastic. (Now you know how I feel about sex I thought.) However, he did try the lasagne and, shock, horror, he absolutely loved it. (I know what you're going to say, but I have and I don't want to anymore.) My vegetarian lasagne was a huge hit and I was spurred on to make other veggie meals. I found a recipe for a vegetable crumble that sounded delicious. Paul's expression when he took his first mouthful said otherwise. Apparently, he drew the line at eating bird seed and the crumble topping had a good sprinkle of nuts and seeds in it. He said the vegetables would have been alright without the topping, maybe as a side dish with a plate of steak and chips. I'd pushed him too far too soon and now I'd be eating crumble pie on my own for the next couple of days.

46

all the best parties

In an attempt to get Tom to be a bit more active, and make myself feel like a better mum, I had enrolled him in a new Street Dance class for six to eight year olds which was starting up in the nearest town. Tom did love his "moves" and, following a class party, his teacher said he had a 'talent which ought to be nurtured'. (I'm not actually sure if he was serious, but he doesn't seem the type to be sarcastic.) Another reason for the dance class was to give Tom the opportunity to try something new. I was determined that he should experience as many different activities as possible so that he could find out what he enjoyed and what he was good at. I never had those sorts of chances and had always regretted not having a go at singing, dancing and acting. I may have been absolutely awful at them all, but at least I would have known it. Don't they say it's the things you *don't do* that you regret? Well, let me tell you, I *didn't do* a hell of a lot of things.

As it was never easy to persuade Tom to try new things, I made sure that Street Dance grabbed his attention by watching a dance talent show on television. He was particularly impressed by one young Street dancer, so much so that he insisted on phoning to vote for him to win. Tom was thrilled when the young boy did win, but absolutely gutted when he realised that it was the dancer who got the £100,000 prize money, and not him.

I don't know if fame and fortune were Tom's motivation, but he agreed to go to the first taster session on the condition that he could just watch and that I'd be there with him. I readily agreed to this; I knew that if I could just get him through the door he would do as the teacher told him. (It was only me and Paul he either ignored or argued with. Our son was six going on sixteen.)

When we arrived at the dance school at the allotted time, I was the one who started to have doubts. It was based in an old church and we were greeted by a wall of freezing cold air and that certain smell that old, cold buildings have. This did not bode well, and I wondered what sort of two-bit outfit I'd hooked up with. I was further alarmed when the other mums and kids started to arrive and seemed oblivious to the state of the place. When I found out that two of the girls were called Morgan and Chanelle, I thought about grabbing Tom's hand and making a run for it. When a couple of boys turned up with studs in their ears I started to have palpitations. I just knew their names would be something like Troy or Tyler or Kane.

Neither Tom nor I fitted in with these people (thank God). They would definitely have been on the 'itchy-head' side of the playground at school. I consoled myself with the knowledge that after the taster session, we need never return.

I wasn't all that surprised when parents weren't allowed in the dance studio itself and felt a momentary pang of guilt that I'd promised Tom I'd be with him. I had told him a little white lie to get him to the class and was counting on him doing as the teacher told him. Sure enough, he went off with the rest of the children without a fuss. Admittedly, he looked as though I was sending him into the depths of hell, but he went to meet his fate without flinching. Thank goodness he had respect for other adults. If I'd asked him, he'd have announced that it wasn't the law and he didn't have to. I wouldn't have been surprised to find he'd already got himself a lawyer lined up.

With Tom gone, I was left alone in the ice-box room with half a dozen women with whom I had nothing in common (except maybe ovaries), facing a forty-five-minute wait. I should have gone off for a coffee somewhere, but I wanted to be there just in case Tom came running out screaming that he was allergic to leg-warmers. So, instead, I sat quietly, hugging my coat around me, looking at the certificates and photographs on the walls, and listening to the other mums' conversations.

'I'm taking Morgan out of her school,' said mum number one, who was wearing imitation UGG boots and far too much blue eyeliner. 'She's really falling behind so I'm sending her to Greenhill instead. The headmaster said she'd really thrive there because it's a very caring and nurturing environment.'

Actually, that's my translation. What she really said was:

'Arm takin' my Morgan ahtuv 'er school... she's really fallin' be-ind so arm sendin' 'er ta Green'ill instead. Vee 'eadmasta said she'd really frive vere 'coz it's a very carin' and nurturin' 'viromen'.'

It soon became apparent that none of these women spoke the Queen's English. One of them had a husband called 'Keef' and I fink anuvver one fought va' Fursday's EastEnders was frilling. Aitches and tees littered the carpet tiles where they had been dropped left, right and centre. The grammar was appalling; it was all 'I done' and 'we was'. I tried not to show my horror, but shuddered inwardly at the thought of Tom mixing with the progeny of these women. I could only hope that the only person speaking inside was the teacher.

I resigned myself to my fate and listened as a discussion of the merits of the various local schools took place. I will translate for your convenience:

'You don't want to send Morgan to Greenhill. That's our local school and it's terrible. My neighbour's children go there and, let me tell you, I wouldn't want my Whitney or my Ronan mixing with them.'

(This was interesting: these women were snobs too. There was clearly a hierarchy of snobbery going on and I felt a little better at how far I looked down my nose at these women as they were obviously doing exactly the same to another social set.)

'Well, that's not the impression I got,' said blue eyeliner. 'The school seemed really nice and they assured me that it would be best for Morgan.'

'No, you want to send her to my Whitney's school – it's lovely, so caring. I think someone's just left Whitney's class too, so they might be able to take her now.'

(I wondered to myself why said child had been removed from the school but kept my mouth shut. I wasn't sure they'd understand me if I did join in the conversation anyway. We didn't appear to have learnt the same alphabet at school.)

What followed can only be described as paradoxical as Whitney's mum (who it turned out was called Sharlene) went on to describe how a boy in her daughter's class had thrown Whitney to the floor and tried to strangle her. This was just one of a veritable catalogue of other such incidents. Mmm, that does sound 'lovely' and 'caring' I thought.

Once Sharlene realised that blue eyeliner wasn't budging on the school issue, she switched the conversation to birthday parties: past and future. From what I could make out, children's parties in their world were all about being bigger and better than anyone else's.

'So, what are you doing for Morgan's birthday this year?' enquired a seemingly innocent Sharlene.

'Well, she either wants a makeover and photo shoot party or a Build-A-Bear party, followed by afternoon tea at Fenwick's,' came the reply.

'Oh yes, we did Build-A-Bear a couple of years ago,' said Sharlene, in a way that made it sound so last season. 'Whitney had a pamper party last year. Thirty-seven girls we had for that one.'

'We had forty-five at Morgan's last birthday party. This year, she wants to invite fifty,' said blue eyeliner, not to be outdone.

'Oh tell me about it! We're planning a Go-Karting party for Ronan and we're having to hire the whole sports centre to fit everyone in. It's costing us a fortune, but what can you do?'

(Jelly and ice cream and pass the parcel for a dozen at home? I thought.)

'Just the party bags alone are going to be a couple of hundred quid,' continued Sharlene.

(What on earth was she putting in them? I wondered. Caviar and diamonds?)

I looked at the floor and prayed that I didn't get invited to join in the conversation. Tom hadn't even had a party for his last birthday as we were away on the family holiday in Norfolk.

Thankfully, just when I thought there might be a catfight over who threw the biggest, best and most expensive kids' parties, the door to the studio opened to mark the end of the lesson. Tom appeared with a big grin on his face. He'd loved the class and definitely wanted to come back next week. I decided there and then to find the nearest available coffee shop before that; no way was I going to risk being caught up in another verbal chavalanche.

47

Hamster house of horror

Oh dear. I knew this day would come. That it was inevitable and could only be put off for so long. That one day I would have to give in. Tom wanted a hamster. I'd managed to fob him off for a good couple of years with battery operated ones, but now he wanted the real thing. I did think having a pet was an important part of childhood – a sort of rite of passage - and I'd shared my childhood with quite a menagerie. I still thought that being a proper mummy was important, not only for Tom's well-being, but for my own sense of self-worth. I wondered if I could persuade Tom to settle for a goldfish, but I suspected not.

I had enormously fond memories of all our pets and couldn't imagine having grown up without them. Except for the hamsters. As much as I loved animals (only that morning I'd rescued a frog from the school playground) I didn't have a great track record with hamsters. Apart from the fact that they're a bit smelly unless you clean them out every five minutes, and that I would undoubtedly be the one cleaning the little stinker out, I was still traumatised by some of the hamster house of horror episodes in my life.

I remember the time I got up one morning to find my pet hamster, George, still and cold and apparently not breathing. He definitely looked dead and I ran to my mum in tears. She checked the little critter, came to the same conclusion and went off to find the inevitable shoe box coffin in which to lay the poor little mite to rest. It was as she was about to commit his body to the earth that mum realised the hamster was still breathing - just. That's when she realised he was hibernating. Oops. George had narrowly missed being buried alive. (Our house must have been bloody freezing back then for a hamster to go into hibernation.) What if I buried Tom's hamster alive? Or worse, what if I thought it was hibernating and it was really dead, and its little corpse was festering in its cage? More counselling please.

Then there was the time I brought the school hamster, Monty, home for the holiday. The beloved class pet was entrusted to my care for a whole week. I wouldn't let my classmates or the hamster down. I would take the very best care of the furry little bundle. I wouldn't let anything happen to it. Then one day I found the little sod had escaped from its cage. I suppose I hadn't shut the door properly. It would have been bad enough if it was my own hamster, but this was the school hamster and I was absolutely distraught. What if I couldn't find it? How would I tell my teacher and my class? They would never forgive me and I would be banned from keeping pets forever. How could I have been so careless? (Being twelve might have had something to do with it.)

My mum was away when this traumatic episode took place in my young life, so I had to go to my step-dad for help. He was cooking fish fingers on a camping stove on the patio at the time (don't ask) and wasn't a big fan of either his step-children or their animals, but I had no choice: I needed a grown up. We searched high and low for Monty, but to no avail, and my step-dad gave up and went back to his camping stove. I was in a right state and carried on looking for Monty. He was nowhere to be seen. I didn't know what to do except wait and hope that he reappeared alive and well before I had to return to school and admit what had happened.

I can remember sitting on the downstairs loo, in the depths of despair and wondering if I should run away from home rather than confess my crime. That's when I heard the scrabbling above my head. My bedroom was directly above the toilet and I raced upstairs to see if Monty had come back. (I think I may even have omitted to flush, let alone put the lid down and wash my hands.) Monty wasn't visible in my room, but I could still hear a faint scrabbling. Oh dear, Monty was under the floorboards. Over the next day or so I tried to entice him out with food, but in the end we had to take the floorboards up to rescue him. Needless to say, my step-dad was not amused.

I should have learnt my lesson then and adopted the motto 'I don't do hamsters'. But no, when I was asked to look after my nephew's hamster many years later I said 'of course, I'd be happy to'. I assured myself that nothing could go wrong; after all I was a responsible adult now and could be relied upon to look after a small furry animal without incident. All I had to do was call in at my sister's house once a day and give Pedro fresh food and water. Easy.

I think I may have said a rude word when I went in on the second day and found the cage empty. I had an awful feeling of déja vu. How could this have happened? Again. Did I have some genetic inability to close hamster cages properly? I felt even worse this time as this was the beloved pet of my young nephew. I had to find it. I had to hope the cat hadn't found it first. I searched everywhere and had just about given up hope when I peeped behind the sideboard on which the cage stood. To my horror, there between the back of the side board and the wall, as flat as the proverbial pancake, was Pedro. I think that was one of the worst moments of my life. And Pedro's, no doubt.

To this day, I don't know what happened to Pedro. I am confessing this awful sin for the first time: on that fateful day, I fished Pedro out, rolled him back into shape a bit, and put him back in his little house, closed the door (properly) and prayed. I didn't know if he was alive or dead but couldn't admit what I had done.

So, you see, me and hamsters just don't mix and my conscience couldn't cope with any more hamster horrors. Personally I think all hamsters should be named Houdini (or Stinky) and returned to the wild. (I have no idea if they ever came from the wild, but hey.) I will re-double my efforts to dissuade Tom from getting a hamster. But they are soooo cute…

48

Facing our addictions

I had lots to do one particular day. I had to make a shopping and 'to do' list. I like lists; I find it very satisfying to cross things off a list when they're done. I have even been known to do something that wasn't on the list du jour and promptly add it to and cross it off the list at the same time. Sad but true. (Besides, such jobs obviously should have been on the list in the first place and omitting them was purely an oversight on my part.) I have also half crossed things off when I can't face finishing them, just to make it look as though I've been productive. Just call me Mrs Half-a-Job.

That day's shopping list looked something like this:

2 sets of ear plugs
2 flak jackets – one large and one small
A one-way ticket to somewhere very far away
1 very funny DVD (must be side-splittingly hilarious) and/or laughing gas
Alcohol. Any. A lot.

I suspected even my Tescos Extra was going to be unable to meet my rather unusual retail requirements on that occasion. I thought I would probably have to improvise somewhat.

My 'to do' list included the following:

Hide sharp knives
Take curtains down and request anti-depressants for Le Wee
Hide the ash tray
Have a long talk with Tom about what he can expect during the coming weeks – perhaps he would prefer to go to boarding school? Make enquiries.
Have divorce lawyer and locksmith on speed dial.

You may be wondering (or not) why I needed such a bizarre selection of items. Well, let me enlighten you: Paul was giving up smoking after thirty-five years. He had tried in the past, but had been so foul-tempered and had such a complete sense of humour failure, that I was soon begging him to start again. He had tried switching to the occasional cigar at times of stress, but was soon smoking as many cigars a day as he had cigarettes. His smoking had always been a bit of an issue between us and I think he was giving up more in an attempt to please me than for himself.

Anyway, this time he was doing it with NHS support and had high-strength patches along with inhalators for emergencies. Unfortunately, the good old NHS didn't seem to offer anything to help family members get through this difficult time; I'd have thought Valium or Prozac would have been available on prescription. Anyway, that was the reason for the odd shopping list. There would undoubtedly be shouting and extreme grumpiness; nothing would be funny anymore and six-year-old boys would be unbelievably irritating. I may have

255

to resort to the occasional Jack Daniels and Coke to cope, and Paul would probably need the odd scotch or two at times of great stress. Terrific, we'd both be non-smoking alcoholics in no time.

I had threatened to send him to live with his parents for a few weeks if he was too vile. They coped with him as a teenager – it'd be a doddle. A one-way ticket for Paul to Timbuctoo was a last resort. Well, it was the last resort I'd think of for a holiday. Wouldn't want him enjoying himself.

Day one of Paul quitting didn't get off to the best start. Apparently just trying to get a patch out of the packet was enough to make him need a cigarette. After he left for work that morning I wondered briefly if it was too soon to phone the locksmith? I was dreading the days and weeks ahead; walking on eggshells was never a comfortable experience (just ask slugs) and I always took it personally when Paul was grumpy. I really did want him to stop smoking though, so I knew I would have to do my best to be supportive and understanding. God help us all.

It was now four days since Paul gave up and I hadn't thought about filing for divorce any more than usual. In fact, he was coping brilliantly and was in a better mood than when he smoked. He was also losing weight and smartening himself up. I could draw only one conclusion: he was having an affair. Either that, or he thought I was and was trying to win me back. (I knew that moisturiser with a hint of foundation would have him worried.) Alternatively, he may have spotted that I was now friends with Dan on Facebook and was feeling insecure. He wasn't the only one.

I had resisted adding Dan as a Facebook friend after I found out about his split from Freya as he was still 'friends' with her and she would be able to see if I added Dan as a friend. Don't ask me why that mattered now they'd split up. The reasons were far too tangled even for me to unravel. Then one day when I was letting curiosity get the upper hand, (if I was a cat, I'd be dead) I noticed that Dan no longer had Freya listed as a friend. My head and heart had a brief tussle. Round one went to my head, but it wasn't long before my heart made a knockout punch and I added Dan to my list of on-line friends. The words 'weaving' and 'tangled web' came to mind even as I sent the request.

I had no idea if Dan would accept my request, or indeed if he ever even thought about me. I waited for his response with a little flutter in my chest, and felt a bigger flutter of excitement when, later that day, he did accept it. God, I was being pathetic, but I didn't seem to be able to help myself. I had lit the blue touch paper and was preparing to play with fire. After all, what were a few burnt fingers between friends?

It had soon become apparent, however, that Dan hardly ever logged on to Facebook and that finger-burning opportunities were going to be very limited. It was some weeks before I saw his name pop up as being on-line and available to chat. At the time, I was chatting to Jess and I asked her if I should say hello. Just seeing his name pop up had made me go all giddy. Before Jess could advise me, and before I lost my bottle, (as well as my marbles and the plot) I had plunged in with a quick 'Hello, stranger, how's life?' message. Highly original, Lucy. Well done. When a reply pinged back almost immediately I nearly passed out. My stomach was doing somersaults for the first time in years (other than after a dodgy curry). It was truly pitiful; the behaviour of a love-struck schoolgirl with a crush on her teacher, not that of a married woman in her forties with a son and two cats.

Dan's reply was a casual 'Not bad thanks' and 'how's the little one?' Hurrah, a question. That meant I could legitimately send another message, which I duly did. Only to find he'd logged off already. I didn't know what to make of it. Why ask a question if you're not going to wait around to hear the answer? I wondered.

My reaction to even this minute amount of contact with Dan was disturbing to say the least. When someone posted a couple of photos with him in on the site a few days later, all the old feelings came flooding back. Either I was suffering from my first asthma attack or seeing Dan's face again had literally taken my breath away. Oh Lucy, Lucy, Lucy, what have you started? You silly, silly girl.

49

Have my jeans shrunk?

I'm ashamed to say that by March, just six months after my breast reduction surgery, I weighed more than I did before the op. I was in danger of having my Weight Watchers' gold membership rescinded and losing sight of my feet again. I only had myself to blame. Well, myself and chocolate. In fact, it wasn't my fault at all. It was entirely chocolate's fault for being so completely scrumptious. If chocolate tasted less divine, my lack of will power wouldn't be an issue. I may have to sue Cadbury's for the flabby state of my stomach. I had a muffin top and suspected it hadn't been caused by water retention, but by double choc-chip muffin retention.

Whatever the cause of my weight gain, I wasn't happy about it. And neither were my jeans. As I seemed unable to give up chocolate, I had decided the only answer was to exercise more. OK, so saying I was going to exercise *more* implied I already exercise *some*, which would be a big fat lie, but you get the gist. To that end, I had roped Sarah in to joining a 'Body Conditioning' class. Unfortunately, I didn't think this would involve applying copious amounts of moisturiser to the afore-mentioned fat bits. However, the lady who ran the class sounded very nice and she promised only a small amount of low-impact aerobics and lots of stretching. Sounded painless enough, and perhaps something even a seasoned exercise-phobe like myself could manage. Hurrah for me. And hurrah for conditioning this very out-of-condition body. Roll on Thursday.

It's now Friday. I don't want to talk about it.

Maybe not. But I do want to have a bloody good moan about it. A 'little bit of low-impact aerobics' my arse. Speaking of which, my arse was feeling the effects of a whole hour of torture. (If you counted the fifteen minutes I spent collapsed in a heap when I could no longer take the pace.) I was even more unfit than I realised and have been forced to eat even more chocolate to cheer myself up. But that wasn't the worst of it: I was out-aerobicised by a pensioner.

When Sarah and I first walked into the hall where the class was held, the only people present, apart from the instructor, were a little old lady who looked about eighty and an old boy maybe ten years her junior. Possibly her toy boy, but I didn't want to think about that. I wondered what on earth we'd walked in to and I knew Sarah was thinking the same thing – at forty-six, Sarah was just two years older than me. It was like a scene out of *Cocoon*. We'd been spotted, however, so there was no sneaking out. Once I'd got over the initial shock of it being day release from the old folks' home, I consoled myself with the thought that at least the class must be pretty easy.

I'm not sure if I was more relieved or terrified when the rest of the class members arrived, and were clearly not escapees from the Twilight Lodge. Sarah and I even knew a couple of the other mums. I would just have to get on with it and do the best I could.

As it turned out, my best was pretty rubbish. I'm not terribly coordinated and asking me to do arm and leg movements simultaneously is pointless. By the time I'd got the hang of a move, the rest of the class had moved on to something else. Sarah, on the other hand, was like a seasoned pro. You can really go off people, can't you? After about fifteen minutes of making a complete tit of myself, I was red in the face and sweating comme un couchon, while Sarah looked as fresh as the proverbial daisy and was barely even 'glowing', let alone sweating like a pig. I had to give up and sit down at that point. Everyone looked a bit surprised as they were clearly not having any difficulty keeping up the pace. Even the cougar and her bit of arm candy were still going. I resisted shouting 'I TOLD YOU I WAS UNFIT'. I don't think I had the puff to shout anything anyway.

I did re-join the class when the exercise mats came out. I figured I'd have a better chance of keeping up with lying down. I did have a modicum more success with the stretching stuff, but found balancing on one leg just made me giggle. And wobble. How on earth did flamingos manage it? I wondered.

The class was due to run for an hour, from nine 'til ten. Somehow, though, whenever I looked up at the clock, it was only ever five past nine. This was easily the longest hour of my life. And the hardest. Even the extras from *Cocoon* and a jolly fat lady had lasted the full sixty minutes. (That sounds bad – I mean jolly as in happy, not as in very.) Either they had been Olympic athletes in former lives, or I was seriously out of shape. I know that round *is* a shape, but it's obviously not the most desirable one for doing an exercise class without the aid of oxygen. I would have to drink serious amounts of Red Bull energy drink or pop a packet of Pro Plus caffeine tablets before next week's torture session.

When ten o'clock finally limped around I flopped back onto

my mat in a less than controlled and elegant manner. I was a sweaty mess; my anti-perspirant had given up and become a pro-perspirant and I felt a complete wreck. Sarah looked just the same as when we'd walked in an hour earlier. If anything, she looked invigorated and had obviously really enjoyed the class. One of us wasn't normal. I suspected it was me. Don't they say that exercise releases endorphins which make us feel good? And that it's addictive? Well, all I can say is that all I got from it were sweaty pits and a headache. Exercisers anonymous would not be getting a call from me any time soon. Or ever, in fact.

50

Jesus goes to Heaven in a cardboard spaceship

Easter was almost upon us and I was pondering the meaning of it all. (Well, it was preferable to pondering the meaning of my life. Though the chocolate quantities were probably about the same.) Did Easter still have much, if any, religious significance to most people? Or was it all about eating chocolate eggs by the lorry load and filling up landfill sites with plastic packaging? The supermarket shelves seemed to have been stocked with Easter eggs since Christmas (bah humbug), and year by year it seemed to become more of a commercial opportunity to be exploited with row upon row of cards, craft kits, dressing-up costumes and Easter bonnets. I was as guilty as the next person of getting on the Easter bandwagon though and had already decorated eggs with Tom for a competition at school and filled a cupboard with half-price eggs from Tescos. Actually, I had filled the cupboard three times. I ate the first two lots of eggs and had to replace them. Oops. To salve my guilty conscience, I put all the packaging aside for junk-modelling. At least when it all finally made its way to the dump, my guilt packaging will have had a full and happy existence being transformed into robots and space ships.

With a sigh, I realised that I was starting to sound middle-aged: a grumpy old woman who got on her soapbox at every available opportunity. I had started to say things like 'it wasn't like that in my day' and 'when I was a girl… ' and shouting criticisms at the television when I didn't agree with something. Mind you, I had nothing on Paul who, since he gave up smoking had become the ultimate grumpy old man and soap box aficionado. Yes, I'm afraid the improvements in Paul after he gave up smoking were only temporary and he was a miserable sod pretty much all the time now. Thank God I had a weekend away with some girlfriends to look forward to.

51

Bath buns

It was Carrie's hen weekend. You remember Carrie? I was her lodger all those pages and nine years ago and we had some really happy times together. Nothing strange about that you may think. But Carrie was marrying Nico. You remember Nico? We had some fun times together when I was between husbands. I said he'd have a happy ending and in a few weeks I will be at his wedding…

Anyway, back to the hen weekend. Twelve of us set off for Bath one morning in late April, in a minibus. Sounds a bit Enid Blyton doesn't it? All we needed was a Collie dog called Timmy and lashings of ginger beer. The sun was shining and we were all in high spirits, in anticipation of a relaxing weekend of thermal spas, shopping and pampering. And possibly a small amount of alcohol consumption and flirting. Not because we wanted to of course, but it was the done thing after all. Be bad form not to stick with tradition. I was just praying there would be no tacky veils and boppy-things-on-heads involved.

Although I didn't know everyone in the party, the group had a good feel to it and I was confident we would all get on famously. (Even though there were more than five of us, and not one Julian or Dick.) Although it had taken me a long time to feel completely comfortable about one of my friends being with one of my exes, I felt secure in the knowledge that nobody else knew about me and Nico. Otherwise it would have been a bit weird and uncomfortable, especially with his mum and sister in the group.

We got as far as the M25 before it got weird and uncomfortable. I don't even remember how the subject came up, but it was now apparent that everyone *did* know about me and Nico. I had rediscovered the art of blushing and experienced a long moment of wishing the ground would open up and swallow me. Although this wouldn't really have worked as we were in a moving vehicle. I didn't think falling into a sink hole on the motorway would have helped anyone. Carrie thought my discomfort was hilarious and regaled the rest of her hens with stories of how I had introduced Nico to her as 'small but perfectly formed' and how 'not every hen takes one of her fiancé's exes on her hen weekend'. I was so embarrassed. I didn't dare look at Nico's mum.

After a few uncomfortable miles (and not just due to the age and nature of the vehicle we were travelling in), with nowhere to hide, I finally concluded that I just had to deal with the fact that everyone knew and let it go. If it didn't bother Carrie, then I wouldn't let it bother me. Much. And anyway, I've always looked good in red. I am the original scarlet woman. A large chunk of the remainder of the journey was spent reminiscing about the good old days when Carrie and I had lived together and how she and Nico had got together during a now (in)famous weekend away.

Said weekend was spent at Pete's house in Lincolnshire. We started out as four friends (with a bit of history between some of us admittedly). I had never told Pete about me and Nico and I assumed that Nico had also kept quiet. There didn't seem to be any point in possibly hurting his feelings. But these things do have a tendency to come back and bite you on the bum, don't they? We had an amazing time, just hanging out together, shopping and sightseeing, drinking and dancing. We even found the Lincoln equivalent of 'Central Perk' from the TV show *Friends* and spent several happy hours lounging around on leather sofas drinking coffee. Leather was a bit of a theme as I remember. It was back in the day when I could still get into my leather trousers and often wore a long black leather coat. I'll never forget the sight of Nico on the Sunday morning when he appeared in Pete's lounge wearing boxer shorts, slippers and my long leather coat. Carrie and I could barely stop laughing long enough to re-Christen him 'Shaft'. I think that moment must have been the clincher for Carrie. Who could resist such a sight? (Although I don't really think Samuel L. Jackson has anything to worry about.)

That memorable morning followed a night of bed-hopping. Calm down - it was all perfectly innocent. Well, it was in my room anyway. Carrie and I were meant to be sharing the double bed in the spare room, but it soon became apparent as we lay in bed like a married couple who'd had a row, that neither of us was comfortable doing so. As I've said before, I'd never been completely relaxed about sharing a bed with a female friend and had only ever made an exception for Freya (and look where that had got me). Carrie obviously felt the same and we had a very drunk and giggly conversation about what to do to resolve the situation. Knowing that Nico and Pete were still downstairs having one last JD and Coke, I made a decision and snuck into Pete's empty bed in the next room. Carrie and I continued our giggly conversation through the wall as we wondered what the guys would do. When Pete came up a little while later, I smiled sweetly and asked if he'd mind sleeping on the sofa. All I know is that Nico didn't sleep on the sofa and that he and Carrie soon became an item.

Initially I was a little bit freaked out at the idea of Nico and Carrie being together and maybe even a little jealous. I suppose my relationship with Carrie did change a bit – for a while – as I came to terms with their being a couple. They were two people I cared about, so ultimately I wanted them to be happy and I found some sort of inner acceptance about the situation.

Back to that Saturday night. As we drove through the streets of Bath, we saw several groups of hens, all decked out in the tackiest of outfits and accessories. Veils and boppy-head-things galore. There was far too much flesh on display in clothes that were much too tight and revealing. We were suitably reassured that we were indeed the most classy and sophisticated group of hens in the city in our tasteful outfits and subtle black sashes which united us as 'Carrie's Hens' on the front and carried our own names on the back. All the other groups wearing sashes had opted for the much less classy white ones.

We had dinner in a restaurant which was very popular with both hens and stags. To say it had a lively atmosphere would be an understatement. The place was awash with pink cowboy hats and feather boas and guys dressed in American military uniforms and mirrored sunglasses. The latter didn't disappoint and were soon serenading a group of girls à la *Top Gun*: 'You never close your eyes anymore when I kiss your lips…' One of the other hens, who looked about twelve, spent a lot of the night in tears. Not sure if they were tears of joy or despair. Maybe her thirteen-year-old boyfriend had got her pregnant

268

and there was a shotgun involved. Or maybe it was the series of dares she'd been given. We watched her as she acquired various items of clothing from several different men at other tables and returned to her hen party victorious, holding her prizes aloft. All I can say is I hope she washed her hands afterwards and I'm bloody glad I don't have a daughter.

After dinner we moved on to a club. They wanted to charge us ten pounds a head to get in, so we got one of the prettier hens to flutter her false eyelashes and get them down to a fiver each. This didn't go down too well with the group of lads in the queue behind us. When they tried the same tactic, the price doubled. I smiled sympathetically at them and we headed into the club. I'd forgotten what a meat-market such places were. They're all very well if you're single and looking, but a bit of a nightmare for old married women like myself. I tried to be invisible and thought I was succeeding until a group of lads latched on to me. Literally. By the sash. They were actually very sweet guys and I was flattered. But I was also stone-cold sober and very out of practice at the whole night club scene. I had thought that previous unwanted attention was largely down to my enormous chest, but, in spite of my vastly reduced assets, I apparently still had 'it' as Carrie observed later.

I did suffer some clothing malfunctions that night. I was wearing the ultimate in magic knickers which basically consisted of a tight tube which rolled from just under my bra all the way down to my thighs. The effect was pretty impressive and it helped me feel more confident about myself and my appearance. Which was all very well until I moved about and the damn thing kept rolling itself up. I had two choices. Either keep fiddling with it or ignore it. I tried to ignore it, but nearly died when some random bloke grabbed my bum. Twice. Talk about a VPL. It was more of an FPL. A feelable panty line. Looking good was bloody hard work and far too stressful. Much as I had loved being single, I don't think my nerves could take it anymore. Imagine meeting someone on a night out whilst wearing all that support, and granny knickers, and then having to get undressed in front of them. Release the bellies. Talk about false advertising. By the time you've removed false eyelashes, make-up, hair extensions, etc. the poor bloke would think he'd gone home with Cinderella and woken up with her much uglier sister. Beer goggles could only take so much responsibility. And then, in my case, there were the scars. The wonky one from my emergency caesarean and my horrid patchwork breasts. Thank God Paul still found me attractive. Either that or he was a really good liar...

The other clothing problem was that my sash kept slipping off my shoulders and I was continually having to step out of it like a pair of unwanted knickers. And every time I did so, my heel caught in the hem of my long skirt. I was not exactly the picture of elegant beauty and composure I had hoped that night. I did manage to make it down the steps to the dance floor without falling head over heels and even managed to have a bit of a dance in my sober state. I just hoped that everyone else was suitably intoxicated and didn't see me making a twit of myself. It was incredibly hot in the basement of the club and after a while I took myself off to join Nico's mum who had found somewhere cool to sit up in the foyer. I was pretty relieved when the others reappeared soon after and we headed back to the cottages. Amazingly we were all in bed (alone, I hasten to add) by midnight. We must be getting old.

I'm relieved to say that the hen weekend didn't get messy. We were all so worried about the long drive in the minibus after our night out that we were all very restrained with the booze. The prospect of being the one who threw up during the journey was a great preventative measure. Two of the girls had actually purchased paella dishes in some cook shop in Bath, which I am convinced had nothing to do with wanting to cook paella when they got home, but rather to act as bowls for catching copious amounts of vomit. The rest of us just put a couple of carrier bags one inside the other and hoped for the best. As it was, nobody was sick, nobody fell over or got taken to A&E, and we all had perfect recall of everything that had gone on. Which was actually surprisingly little. I'm willing to bet some of the other groups of hens didn't get off so lightly.

The rest of the weekend was pretty blissful. We went to the Thermae Spa, a historic spa where we bathed in naturally hot mineral-rich water and floated in the stunning rooftop pool, overlooking the rooftops and spires of the beautiful city of Bath. It's true that my pleasure at seeing the view was slightly marred by me being very aware that my fellow hens were mostly much skinnier than me. Anticipating this, I'd bought a swimming costume with a tummy control panel for the occasion. Unfortunately it didn't cover the scars under my arms from my breast reduction, so not only was I trying to hold my tummy in, but I was also trying to keep my arms down by my sides to hide my scars.

We also had therapists come to the cottages to give massages and manicures. We took it in turns to soak in the Jacuzzi in the unseasonably warm sunshine, with views of stunning country-side and chickens pecking in the yard around us, nary a cock in sight. It really was a perfect location. I hoped that Carrie's and Nico's life together would be just as perfect. I also hoped, though, that they wouldn't ask me to be a bridesmaid.

52

It's curtains for the carpet

Now that winter was over (for this week at least. What was going on with the British weather? It was May for heaven's sake) Paul and I had decided to rip up the lounge carpet which was so old and worn that even my amazing Dyson vacuum cleaner couldn't pick up the bits. I simply couldn't stand it another day. When I'd gone to the trouble of vacuuming a carpet, I wanted it to look as though I'd vacuumed it.

From time to time, as you may have noticed, I get mildly obsessed about something and convince myself that remedying it will give me some sort of temporary peace of mind. Of course, it was only ever a distraction from the real problems in my life: what the heck would make me happy for more than five minutes? But any distraction was a welcome one, as I couldn't even begin to face the real issues. Anyway, the lounge carpet was my current bugbear/diversion.

We were hoping to find some decent floorboards which could be sanded and stained, and were thrilled when we started to peel back the carpet and found exactly that. The only problem was that said lovely floorboards were interspersed with concrete. We should have known. Ours was one of those houses where nothing was ever straightforward or easy. Our house was a metaphor for our marriage…

We decided to go ahead anyway, and the carpet was cut up

and consigned to the skip. Was this prophetic I wondered? We planned to redecorate the lounge and then buy a new carpet later in the year, before the weather got cold again. (August probably.) I had a rough idea of the style and colour I wanted for the room, and set off on a mission to find curtains or paint to get the scheme started. Another welcome distraction activity.

This was my usual haphazard way of redecorating a room. I would find something I loved – be it a pair of curtains, a cushion or a picture – and work the rest of the scheme around it. This time it was a pair of curtains I fell in love with. They were beautiful sage green faux silk, and I simply had to have them. They looked beautiful when we hung them on the new (faux) silver curtain pole. For about five minutes. I fell out of love with the curtains the way I fall out of love with everything. They had looked so much better in the shop somehow. And it wasn't the colour I had fixed in my mind. It had to be celadon. Nothing else would do. I'd made up my mind.

So, down came the sage green curtains. I decided they would look good in the spare bedroom, which could be tweaked with very little effort by adding a gold throw to the bed. Ta dah! One beautiful green and gold guest room.

So, mission number two. This resulted in some tester pots of paint. And another pair of curtains. Well, they were an absolute bargain and had just about every colour under the sun in the floral design, so they couldn't fail to go with whichever paint I eventually chose. Pair of curtains number two was now hanging in the hall and looked lovely. Admittedly I did have to go and buy a second pair for the landing…

The good news was I had definitely decided on duck egg paint for the lounge. I know I said I wanted celadon, but it wasn't a million miles away. We had also picked out an accent colour for the room and I was now on a hunt for purple curtains. What a relief to have the colour decisions made. The rest would be a doddle.

I have just bought the fourth and final pair of curtains for the lounge, following a virtual mission on the internet. They were described as aubergine and looked to be the perfect shade of purple.

Anyone want to buy some faux silk purple curtains?

The trouble was, I just didn't like them when they were up. The colour was OK, but they let through far too much light and just looked cheap. I couldn't return them as I've already pulled the strings. I would probably use them elsewhere in the house at a later date, and then have to redecorate whichever room they ended up in.

Paul had started to despair of me and my curtain buying. Every time I went out anywhere he would ask me if I had bought more curtains. Men simply don't understand the importance of getting the finishing touches just right though, do they? Most of them would be happy with an old sheet fixed up at the window with drawing pins. Which was just as well as I was no nearer to finding my perfect purple pair. I resisted the urge to retort that at least I was only changing my mind about window coverings, and that I knew women who'd changed their minds about husbands as many times. I couldn't help thinking Paul should be grateful it was only curtain strings I was pulling.

In desperation, Paul and Tom accompanied me on a perfect purple curtain buying mission. We didn't find any curtains, but instead came home with a gorgeous deep-purple rug which we were all stroking in the shop with rather too much pleasure. I think if we hadn't purchased the rug, we would've been escorted from the premises by security for lewd behaviour, and banned from the home furnishings department for life. It was a lovely rug though, and should anything happen to the cats, we will still have something nice to stroke. I did fear that Paul had other plans for the rug. He should be used to being disappointed by now.

As for the curtains, I had tracked down another shop (where I would not be recognised) and had successfully acquired the perfect pair of curtains for my duck egg and purple lounge. They were teal. And the wrong length. But apart from that they were absolutely perfect.

I resolved the two accent colour problem by buying cushions in both teal and purple and was very pleased with the final result. Apart from the patchwork concrete and wooden floor. And as for the curtains being too long? Well, they looked so much classier floor length and I was confident that Louie would have no issues with them as they couldn't possibly smell of cat wee. Besides, the shop had sold out of shorter ones. Maybe we were not the only household with a cat who liked to wee up curtains.

Oh well, at least they're machine washable I told myself as I bundled the curtains of great gorgeousness into the drum with a good dose of biological liquid and a dash of disinfectant. Unfortunately Le Wee had expressed his dislike of my latest choice of window dressing in his usual disgusting manner. As a temporary solution (and when machine washing had failed to shrink them sufficiently) we swagged the curtains over decorative hooks to keep them off the floor. They looked lovely; the drawback being that we couldn't. Draw them back that is. No, we couldn't close the curtains at night for fear of Le Wee doing le wee on them. It was unfortunate that our lounge window looked out onto a public footpath, but that should at least scupper any romantic plans Paul had for the rug for the time being at least. Every cloud and all that.

53

a fete worse than death

Summer was almost upon us once more and, according to the weather people, we were in for a scorcher. I was hesitant to believe the meteorological men, however, and would still be packing jumpers and cagoules along with the swimsuits and flip flops for the annual family holiday in August.

I sincerely hoped the forecast was accurate for the day of the school summer fete-worse-than-death (as Paul called it) as I was again running a couple of stalls and it would be a pretty miserable affair if the weather was... well... miserable. I would definitely be taking a gazebo to erect over the table which would act either as sun shade or umbrella. Last year was incredibly hot and the fete did really well – especially the bar and the wet sponge throwing. Funny that.

I ran the raffle last year and managed to get some pretty good prizes donated by sending out begging letters to various local companies. I think getting them signed by 'Tom, aged five' might have helped there. This year however, it was all my own work (Lucy, aged forty-four) and I had again managed to procure a decent selection of goodies. I just hoped the draw wasn't the anti-climax that it was last time: we'd got storm-troopers to hand out the prizes but none of the winners were present when we made the announcements. This year I had asked that the *grand* draw be made earlier in the hope that more winners would still be at the fete. If not, I may have to re-name it the completely-anti-climactic-and-why-did-I-bother-I'm-not-doing-it-next-year prize draw.

The other stall I'd been persuaded to run was a water or wine game. In a nutshell, you had a table full of wrapped wine bottles, some of which contained wine and some water. You paid your money and took your pick. Sounds straightforward enough, right? Right. Once you've sussed out where on earth you're going to get that many empty wine bottles with screw tops from and the logistics involved in filling, wrapping and transporting said bottles. Not to mention disposing of them after the fete.

The supply problem was solved by asking a local publican to save his empties for a few weeks. Not even a seasoned alcoholic was going to be able to drink the sort of quantity I was after. And if I tried I would certainly be in no fit state to man anything at the fete. Unless they were thinking of having a yucky dip and could provide me with a bucket or six. Consequently, my garage was full of boxes of wine bottles and smelled like a rather inferior winery. I only had to wash, fill, re-cap, mark as water and wrap the one hundred and fifty bottles and get them to the top field at school. Piece of cake. Ooh, yes please, I'll have banana. I couldn't understand why they wouldn't let me run the cake stall this year. Something about the profits. And eating.

The day of the fete dawned a little overcast, but we remained hopeful that the skies would clear and the sun come out. Which I'm sure they did. Somewhere a bit nearer the Equator. We, on the other hand, were treated to an extravaganza of wind and rain. The gazebos did their best to withstand the elements, but

279

it was a bit of a washout. The bar would have done better had they had been serving soup and hot chocolate, and the wet sponges were about as appealing as a slap round the face with a month-old kipper. At one point the gazebo over the cake stall took off across the field, taking the 'guess-the-weight-of-the-cake' cake with it. (Luckily the vicar's wife subsequently won this and was far too polite to say anything.)

The water and wine stall was a success I'm pleased to say, although it was pretty tricky to keep the five to one ratio of water to wine on the table as we had no way of telling the difference between them once they were wrapped. Still, it did mean we couldn't be tempted to cheat and give our friends the nod when they picked up a goodun. Or, of course, do the same in reverse to any non-friends.

The raffle did OK too, although the prizes did get a little soggy and maybe one or two of the names and phone numbers may have run a teensy bit making it nigh on impossible to contact the winners. It didn't make a blind bit of difference that we drew the raffle earlier; still no bugger was there to collect their prize, which meant that I had to take most of the prizes home and try to make contact with people by phone. I can only apologise to all the people I called in error due to ink running issues, and to all those whose names I got wrong for the same reason. Then there was the usual problem of people only writing on the top stub and leaving the rest blank. One particularly bright spark completed their details on the first ticket and simply wrote 'Same' on all the subsequent ones. D'oh. They really didn't deserve to win a prize, unless it was free entry to the pool. The one they remove your genes from.

After the sunny stand-up success of the previous year's fete, the whole thing was a bit wet and floppy. I don't think the children having a go on the tea cup ride were expecting the cups to be full. Milk and two in mine please. The display arena would have been more suited to mud wrestling than cheer-leading and dancing. Actually, I may suggest mud wrestling for next year. I reckon that would improve the turn out no end if we advertised it properly. Mind you, the tug of war was pretty funny, as was the marching band which was in constant danger of going over like a pack of dominoes. We had the emergency services on hand though, so not to worry. Besides they were getting free Tip Top drinks as payment. What more could they want? Maybe they'd like to put forward a mud-wrestling team next year.

54

Moans and groans and chocolate biscuits

September arrived – another long school holiday survived, and sighs of relief from us mums as the kids were dropped back at school. We were having coffee at Claire's after school drop off. She'd just had a new kitchen fitted and had invited us round to admire it. Sarah and I were reluctant to go as we both hated our kitchens and knew we were going to be terribly jealous. However, any opportunity for a gossip was too good to miss. Besides, Claire always had particularly chocolatey chocolate biscuits and proper coffee.

Having oohed and aahed over the kitchen, Sarah and I had a good moan about the sorry state of ours and went and sat in Claire's equally lovely lounge, while Claire went off to make coffee. Now I'm not saying that we liked teasing Claire… not at all. We loved it. When she came back into the lounge, carrying a tray of coffee and biscuits, Sarah and I were talking in hushed tones, with our best serious faces on. Just as Claire put the tray down on the coffee table, Sarah and I both rolled up our sleeves to reveal deep scratches on our arms:

'Oh my God, Sarah, not you too? How long has it been going on?' I asked, reaching out and putting my hand on her shoulder in a show of solidarity.

Giving a little sniff, Sarah fumbled in her handbag for a tissue: 'I don't know. Not long. A couple of weeks maybe,' she stammered.

I risked a peep at Claire's face. She looked absolutely horrified.

'What made you do it? Do you know what triggered it?' I asked quietly.

'I'm not sure. I've just been feeling that I'm not coping. Gary's been doing even less than usual – if that's possible – and I just needed a release.' This was Oscar-nomination stuff.

'God, I know what you mean,' I sympathised, trying to keep a straight face. 'I just couldn't stand it any longer.'

By this time, Claire had found her tongue: 'Oh my God! Are you two self-harming? Surely things can't be that bad?' she asked in shocked disbelief. 'Why didn't you say something sooner?'

It was no good. I couldn't bear to see Claire look so worried and upset. Time to 'fess up.

'Do you feel better now, though, Sarah? Now that the pruning's all done?' I asked.

Claire looked confused.

'Absolutely!' confirmed Sarah. 'Just wish I wasn't so desperate for a tan that I pruned the roses and hawthorn wearing a sleeveless top.'

Claire still looked confused.

I laughed. 'If you ever did any gardening, Claire, you'd know that we look as though we've taken razors to our arms, when what we've actually been doing is trying to get a tan while we garden.'

We could see the penny finally dropping. 'You cows!' said Claire.

'Moo!' Sarah and I said in unison.

When Charlie and Zoe arrived the subject soon switched to school matters. (Neither of them was a keen gardener.) This made a change from men matters. Or men not matters as was more often the case.

The latest thing to wind everyone up at school was that the children had to dress up for 'Zambian Day' when St. George's day had been completely overlooked. To be honest I wasn't really bothered as long as Tom had something in his drawers in whatever colours were required, but some of the mums were terribly patriotic. (As opposed to racist, I hasten to add.) This sort of thing always wound them up. It had been the same when the kids learnt about the festival of Diwali, which as far as Zoe knew was not on the Christian calendar. I'd given up pointing out that the school taught what it was required to teach and had to take an inclusive approach to the subject of religion. Instead I just nodded and said 'Mmm' occasionally. They didn't need to know that I was actually making appreciative noises to show my approval of Claire's choice of biscuit.

Next came PE kits, another thing the mums liked to gripe about. Owing to their little ones coming home with some of their PE kit missing or wearing other children's clothes, the mums all seemed convinced that the teacher should have no problem keeping track of their small charges' clothing. I kept my mouth shut knowing that I had a hard time keeping on top of Tom's uniform situation without having twenty-nine others to contend with. Personally I thought the teachers deserved medals just for turning up in the mornings at all, and that if they took responsibility for all our children's belongings they wouldn't actually have time to teach them anything.

55

(Face)book my place in hell

I now had fifty-seven 'friends' on Facebook, including several of the mums. And I knew people who had hundreds of FB friends. Perhaps the number of friends you had on Facebook had a direct correlation with personal happiness? Maybe if I had loads of social media followers I'd be happier? I wasn't convinced of this, but maybe the illusion of being 'liked' by so many people could bring a kind of delusional happiness? I barely knew some of my 'friends' as it was; some were friends of friends, others were friends of friends' friends, many worked at my old firm (but didn't work there when I did) and some were just friends because they were needed as farm neighbours or mob members. It was a bizarre concept all round and I did wonder about the psychology of it all. I feared Facebook was the enemy of someone like me and could be used for virtual self-harming – I would probably never 'unfriend' toxic people from FB any more than I would delete them from my phone, or remove them from my psyche.

I was always terribly grateful when someone sent me an invitation to be their friend and invariably accepted just to swell my numbers and not look like Billy-No-Mates. I did wonder how people managed to continually acquire new 'friends'. They must have terribly exciting lives to be constantly meeting new people. Either that or they have extremely low self-esteem and needed the reassurance of pages and pages of FB pals to bolster their egos.

There were people who I would like to befriend on a social networking site simply so I could be a nosey parker and keep up to date with their antics. But then I worried that all my other 'friends' would know that I'm friends with that person and would judge me for it. Oh it was all so damned convoluted. For example, I would like Freya to become number fifty-eight (or Bitch) so that I could see what she was up to. I knew that was pretty twisted and that a) I shouldn't care what she was up to and b) it was pretty self-destructive, but that was me. However, if I invited Freya to be my friend, Dan would know and then he might think badly of me. How screwed up was that?

I knew I shouldn't be 'friends' with either of them, Facebook or otherwise, and that it wasn't good for my mental health to want to be, but I couldn't seem to help myself. I pushed my self-destruct button years ago and unfortunately the damn thing came off in my hand. Clearly I was in need of psychological help. Or a lobotomy. Until then, however, I would continue to befriend random strangers and tend my virtual farm. That reminds me, I have a crop of pumpkins to harvest and eggs to collect. Back in a mo.

Sorry about that. Took a little longer than anticipated as I had a little virtual chat with one of my 'friends'. Actually, make that a friend of a friend who I haven't seen for years on account of the fact that he used to live with my ex, and we're not really friends.

Tim once shared a house with Dan and Mike, so naturally, as Dan's friend, he and I no longer saw each other after Dan and I split up. That was before social networking of course.

Now we were the modern equivalent of pen pals, and Tim was a way of finding out what was happening with Dan. As well as being a very nice person of course. And pretty funny too.

Well, Tim dropped me a line yesterday to tell me he'd been invited out for a curry with Dan and Mike and their girlfriends. As a confirmed bachelor, Tim didn't get invited to 'coupley' things very much. The rest of the chat went something like this:

Me: 'How about I come as your date. That would be hilarious.'

Tim: 'Yeah, great idea. We could arrive a bit late and breathless, with our hair all mussed up.'

Me: 'And our tops inside out or buttoned up wrong.'

Tim: 'Maybe we should announce our engagement too.'

Me: 'And hand out wedding invites. After I've flashed the most enormous diamond in Dan's girlfriend's face.'

Tim clearly thought I was joking about going with him, but part of me was deadly serious. I knew that I wouldn't actually go as I had a PTA meeting that night. Oh, and a husband and son to consider of course, but there was definitely a little red devil sitting on my shoulder telling me to do it. The slightly grubby, tired-looking angel perched on my other shoulder was doing his best to persuade me that it was a terrible idea and could only lead to heartache; he knew he'd only won this round thanks to the meeting I had promised to attend. Damn the PTA.

Anyway, I told Tim to have a good time, to give Dan my love and stick his tongue out at Mike for me. I said I would expect a full report the next day.

The following morning, unable to wait for Tim to get in touch, I sent him a message asking how the evening had gone.

Tim: 'It was good thanks.'

Me: 'Any gossip for me?'

Tim: 'Er…'

Me: 'Tim…?'

Tim: 'Well… Dan announced that he and Rebecca have got engaged.'

Me: 'Blimey that was fast work. I wonder if Freya knows?'

Tim: 'I doubt it. And anyway, why should she care? She left him.'

Me: 'Tim, Tim, you have a lot to learn about women. Just because we don't want a man anymore, that doesn't mean we want them to stop wanting us or to want someone else. Got that?'

Tim: 'Er… yeah… clear as mud. You women are really pretty screwy you know.'

Me: 'Tell me about it.'

However, I was relieved to find that I didn't feel overly suicidal at the news of Dan's betrothal, but it had further dashed any lingering hopes over Dan still having feelings for me. I wondered again if Freya did know? Maybe now would be a good time to invite her to be my 'friend' and then just casually drop the news into the 'conversation'? I know. I'm a bad person and will go to hell. At least the summers would be hot.

If I was really bad, I could post a comment on Dan's page offering my congratulations as Freya might see that too. I can't do that though as I'm not supposed to know and it might drop Tim in it. And then he might not want to be my 'friend' anymore and I would lose my gossip-monger. Oh it's all so complicated. And I really must look up 'friend' in a thesaurus because you must be getting as sick of reading it as I am of writing it.

As I couldn't think of a way of getting to Freya directly, I sent Jess, who had stayed in the UK so that doctors could monitor her heart problem, a message telling her about the engagement. Jess had Freya as an FB chum and might know more. I would wait patiently for a response from Jess and if I hadn't heard from her in five minutes, I'd text her.

56

The perfect pink

The end of summer also meant Carrie and Nico's wedding was almost upon us. I was determined to really go to town on an outfit (and indeed *for* an outfit) rather than just rootling through my wardrobe for something that would 'do'. I had also promised Carrie that I would break my no hat rule as she was a serious hat person. What was I thinking? Hats looked bloody awful on me. I had the wrong hair. Or the wrong face. The wrong something, that's for sure. Attitude perhaps?

The prospect of dress shopping no longer filled me with dread as I was now a size twelve all over. Gone were the days when I could only wear separates to accommodate my enormous knockers. I can't tell you how good it felt to pick a size twelve shift dress off the peg and know that there was a chance it might actually fit me. Well, actually I can. I just did. But I can't emphasise enough how amazing it feels. Well, actually I can. I just have. Yes, OK, Lucy we get the idea. Admittedly I still had to be a bit careful about the cut of a dress as my scars could be an issue, but even so I had so much more choice now.

So, finding a dress for the wedding wasn't a problem. Nor was finding the right shoes: I found a perfect pair of pink satin sandals which exactly matched the colour of the embroidery on the dress. Even a matching cardigan and the right jewellery came easily. Then there was the hat. Me and my big mouth. Maybe that was the problem.

However, a promise was a promise and I had dutifully been to every shop in the county which might possibly stock hats. And indeed many which don't. Twice. I have tried on every vaguely suitable hat in the county. Twice. They are all the wrong pink. Every last one of them. I was despairing of ever finding the right hat and, to that end, I have borrowed one from Carrie in a slightly less wrong pink than some and have bought a lovely purpley-pink one which was far too purple to be considered pink. But I really liked it and it was cheap. And the sales assistant didn't snigger when I tried it on. The fact that I would probably never have an occasion to wear it was irrelevant. It was like the curtains all over again and I had seen the despairing look on Paul's face every time I came home with another bag. He should be grateful I wasn't coming home with hat boxes, because they don't give you boxes unless you buy something a bit more high-end.

In a last-ditch attempt to find the perfect hat, I had set off once more for a well-known department store. I had with me my pink shoes for colour-matching and a steely determination to succeed. After an hour's drive I parked the car and headed in to the shop. By some fluke I came in the door to the café. Taking this as a sign – it was, it said 'Café' – I fortified myself with a coffee and an almond Danish. Yum. Now I was ready to do battle.

I lost.

And that was how the shop assistant found me. Defeated, battle-fatigued and clearly suffering from PTSD (Post Traumatic Shopping Disorder), clutching a pink sandal, rocking backwards and forwards and close to tears.

And that was how I came to be wearing a big pink flying saucer on my head come the wedding day. Having agreed that all the hats were indeed the 'wrong pink' the shop assistant (I will be using my contact at the Vatican to recommend her for Sainthood) disappeared for a few minutes, only to return with afore-mentioned flying saucer in EXACTLY THE RIGHT PINK. OK, so it wasn't exactly a hat, it was more of a fascinator, but it was a big fascinator, and I loved it. I would call it a hatinator. And it was perfect.

Paul still wasn't smoking at this point. It had been about three months and he was finding it pretty hard going. As were the rest of us. He was reluctant to admit that he was putting on weight as a result, until he tried his suit on and couldn't do the trousers up. He admitted that even if he crash dieted there was no way he was going to get the button to meet the hole. Oh there's a handy metaphor for our life together, I thought.

So, one new suit later and a cool shirt and waistcoat combo for Tom and we were all kitted out for the wedding.

Carrie and Nico were holding their wedding celebrations across an entire weekend and most of the guests were staying at the venue for the duration; me, Paul and Tom included. The venue was a stately home in the Kentish countryside, with gatehouse and outbuildings providing additional guest accommodation. We'd been looking forward to the 'mini-break' for ages and Carrie and Nico had gone to an awful lot of trouble to make sure their guests were well-looked after, right down to leaving chocolates on our pillows. I resisted the urge to sneak into the other rooms and snaffle the chocs.

We all arrived for a barbeque on the Friday night, and

were greeted by Nico wearing an apron bearing the words: 'Prick with a fork', which Tom thought was hilarious (once I'd explained to him the dual meaning of prick and got him to swear not to repeat it to his friends. Yes, I got him to swear he wouldn't swear. How does that work exactly? I would never understand the English language.)

The weather wasn't especially kind to us on the day of the actual wedding. I was soon cursing the wet grass and my ruined shoes. It was my own fault. For once when the shop assistant had asked if I wanted to purchase protective spray with the shoes, I had said yes. Regrettably, I'd been too lazy to actually use it on the shoes and they were now stained as much as my conscience. Thankfully, we'd brought umbrellas so at least my hatinator stayed dry. Although when the wind picked up it did threaten to take off and return to its home planet.

Carrie looked absolutely beautiful and there wasn't a dry eye in the chapel as she made her entrance. (And not just because it was raining.) Nico definitely filled up and looked as pleased and proud as punch as he saw his bride approaching. I had a tear in my eye as I watched my dear friend and my one-time friend-with-benefits tie the knot, but I was relieved to find it was a tear of happiness for them and their future together and nothing to do with my past. It was good to know that at least one of my exes wasn't taking up inappropriate head space.

Later at the reception, Paul was soon looking relaxed with a glass of red wine in his hand. I knew he was anxious about controlling the desire to smoke. It was the first real test he'd had of being in a social setting, and that the long-standing association he'd had between a drink and a fag was going to be a tough one to break. I did notice that whenever the chief bridesmaid lit up he moved to her side and inhaled gratefully. I knew exactly what he was doing and wasn't the least bit bothered, but I think everyone else who noticed thought he had a bit of a thing for the bridesmaid and felt rather sorry for me. The poor jilted wife. Ha! If only they knew that he was only after her for her second-hand smoke.

Unfortunately for the bridesmaid in question, the more Paul drank the more touchy feely he got when he sidled up to her. Apparently he patted her on the bottom a few times. Well, who could blame him? She did have a very nice bottom. Paul did tend to turn into a bit of a dirty old man when drunk and he had a laugh a bit like Sid James in the *Carry On* films. I think this weekend was the most drunk I've ever seen him though: a little flash of what he must have been like before responsibilities got the better of him. And if anyone else got a little flash, then I apologise on Paul's behalf.

My suspicions about Paul's degree of drunkenness were confirmed the next morning when I realised he was actually suffering from some memory loss. He could only remember up until 10 p.m. I saw a perfect opportunity to wind him up, and I had the perfect ammunition.

'So, do you think you'd better apologise to Maria when you see her?' I asked. (Maria was the smoking bridesmaid. And yes she was pretty hot.)

'What on earth for?' enquired my butter-wouldn't-melt husband.

'Well, mainly for touching her bum at every opportunity,' I said with a perfectly straight face. 'Carrie told me all about it.'

'I did no such thing!' Paul said with as much indignation as he could muster.

'Oh come off it, you know what you're like when you've had a few. And Carrie certainly wouldn't lie to me. You were all over Ria like a rash.'

'I most certainly was not.' More indignation.

'I suppose you're going to tell me you didn't dive on top of that pile of girls – Maria included – when they were having group photos taken?' was my next shot across Paul's bow.

'Now I know you're winding me up, I know I didn't do that. I wouldn't.' Paul was vehement in his denial.

'And there's no way you would cop a feel of Hannah's tits either, I suppose?' OK so now I was pushing it. 'I wonder if we can get fingerprints from chocolate?' I mused. 'I think you'd been at the chocolate fountain just before that encounter.'

Paul blanched at this, to give him his credit, and absolutely refused to believe it.

'OK,' I said 'but just you wait 'til the photos appear. And there you'll be, lying on the floor with your leg over Maria and Hannah. I will accept your apology in diamonds. Or chocolate.'

I think Paul muttered something about 'at least I got my leg over' and he continued to believe it was a wind-up and that I was taking advantage of his memory lapse. Then the photos appeared on Facebook. And he didn't have a leg to stand on.

Now he is at my mercy as he's not quite sure if I was joking about his boob with Hannah…

57

The breakthrough

I finally heard back from Jess. She sounded pretty gobsmacked about the news of Dan's engagement. Apparently Freya hadn't mentioned it in any of her Facebook updates so we were working on the assumption that she didn't know. I hadn't asked Jess if she was going to tell Freya. It wasn't really our news to tell after all. But the evil part of me would so have liked to be the one to tell her. Or at least be a fly on the wall when she heard.

Deciding that we needed a full and frank discussion of the whole situation, Jess and I arranged to meet up. Because I was so eager to see her I arrived early and was on my second Americano when she turned up at our favourite coffee shop in Maidstone the following Saturday. I'd also munched my way through an enormous almond pastry. (Well, we all had our croissant to bear, I sighed, as I silently admonished myself for my complete and predictable lack of will power where food was concerned.)

Once we'd hugged hello and Jess had ordered her skinny latté, no sugar, definitely no cake, we sat back in the leather arm chairs with contented sighs. After a quick catch up on life in general, and Jess's health in particular (the doctors had decided on a watch and wait strategy with her heart), the conversation soon turned to Freya. It turned out that Jess hadn't had any contact with her and still had no idea if Freya knew about

Dan's news. After both admitting that we'd quite like to see her reaction when she found out, it didn't take long for us to decide that it was really none of our business and that we shouldn't get involved.

Jess looked at me thoughtfully. 'You're not really over him are you?'

I thought about this for a moment. 'Until recently I thought I wasn't, but you know, Jess, I'm not sure I feel much at all about Dan getting married again.'

Jess nodded slowly. 'That must be a good thing,' she said.

I smiled. 'Yes, it must be. I think I'm kind of over the whole Dan thing. It seems unlikely after obsessing about him all these years, but I don't feel particularly upset.' Saying these words aloud was as much a revelation to me as it was to Jess.

'Now that really is something,' Jess said in amazement. (She had been the recipient of an awful lot of 'Lucy loves Dan forever' mooning after the break-up. No, I don't mean I bared my bottom at all and sundry whilst shouting 'Lucy loves Dan'. I mean the yearning, pining, infatuation kind of mooning. My forty-four-year-old bottom was definitely not fit for public consumption. Hah! Gotta love the English language eh?)

'I'm really not that bothered, Jess,' I added in disbelief.

'That's good. Maybe now you can move on with your life and find some real happiness – contentment even.' Jess sounded so happy for me. She was probably relieved that she wouldn't have to put up with all the mooning too.

'Mmm… maybe,' I said, half-heartedly. 'Honestly though, I don't know if I'll ever be content with my life. I know in my head that the grass isn't really greener on the other side, but I don't seem to be able to convince my heart of that fact.'

'How *are* things at home? Is it any better between you and Paul?'

'It's the same. We rub along OK – it's not like we fight or argue or anything – but we're just people who live in the same house and have a child together. Paul deserves so much better than I give him. He's never done anything except love me,' I sighed.

'Don't beat yourself up, Luce. You can't force yourself to have feelings for someone.' Jess squeezed my arm as she could see I was getting emotional.

'I know, but I can't leave him - for his sake as well as Tom's – and it's getting harder and harder to keep up the act; pretending to be happy when inside I feel like I'm dying. The thought that this is it for the rest of my life is pretty scary, Jess, and I know now that I've been trying to cope with my marriage by focusing on other things.'

'What other things do you mean?'

'Oh, I dunno, anything and everything really. Getting a puppy, changing the décor. Stupid stuff that really shouldn't matter, but somehow acts as a diversion from the real problems. I know taking my mind off things doesn't really work, but it's easier to be unhappy myself than to make others unhappy. Does that make sense?'

'Yes, it makes sense, but it's pretty sad. Don't you deserve happiness too?'

'Yes, I think I do, but it's not that easy.'

'Lucy, I think you need to give some serious thought to what you want out of life and whether your marriage to Paul is ever going to be enough.'

'I know, but there's Tom to consider.'

'Tom will be fine – he's a smart kid and he'll want you to be happy. Yes, Paul would be gutted, but he'd get over it and, like you said, he deserves better. Can't you tell Paul how you're feeling?'

'I know you're right, but how do you start a conversation like that? Once that can of worms is opened, there's no putting the lid back on. I'm scared, Jess.'

'I'm not saying it would be easy, but do you really want to be having this same conversation six months, a year, down the line?'

'No, of course not. I'm just not convinced I will ever find anyone better than Paul. I'm the problem, Jess, not him. I don't think I'm cut out for long-term relationships, so what's the point in trying to find another one? It'll only ever end with me being unhappy again. Isn't it better to try and find a way of making life bearable?'

'That's up to you, Luce, but it sounds pretty lousy to me.'

'Maybe I just need to find something for me. Go back to work or take up a hobby – something that's just about me, Lucy, not Paul's wife or Tom's mum. Maybe I can find some kind of fulfilment that way? It might just make everything else a bit better.'

'Worth a try, I guess.' Jess didn't sound convinced.

'I love Tom so much – he's my reason for getting out of bed in the morning, but being a mum isn't enough,' I said with a sigh. 'Anyway,' I said, feeling that a change in subject was advisable, 'being over Dan feels bloody good!'

'About time too! I never did know what you saw in him,' Jess joked.

Being over Dan was a definite break through. Perhaps I was

finally ready to put the past behind me. To spring clean that over-crowded corner of my brain where all my exes lurk, and make room for something less destructive.

After Jess and I had put the world to rights, we hugged good-bye and walked back to our cars. I drove home in a thoughtful mood. I don't really remember the journey – I think I was on some sort of auto-pilot, as I mulled over the conversation I'd just had with my wise young friend. It had made me accept that something had to change if I was ever to find that elusive thing called happiness, and that only I could make that change come about. By the time I pulled onto the drive, I had made up my mind.

I was going to find a way of making my marriage work – it was too important; Paul and Tom were too important. I was the problem and I must find the solution.

I'd thought for a long time that the problem was other people, but I now realised that wasn't so. I needed to find myself and probably by now I had to some extent. Running away from my problems wasn't going to solve them. Looking back, I'd done rather a lot of running away from things – from men, from my big breasts, from not being a mum. It was now time to stop running, and to embrace everything I had: to appreciate what I had and make it work.

Mentally revisiting my adult life, and all my vain attempts to find contentment, I had to admit a painful truth: the grass was not greener on the other side. I had wasted so much of my time looking over my neighbour's fence at their bright green lawn and going equally green with envy, that I had failed to see it was a dye job. It was all for show – an illusion. What I needed to do was focus on the lawn of my own life; pull out the odd dandelion, scatter a bit of seed, and who knew what I might find. I had been so busy looking at what I *didn't* have, that I had failed to see the wonderful things that I *did*.

Lucy Shaw still wasn't completely sure what would make her happy, but she had a much better idea now than she did before. The future was bright. Bright green!

THE END

acknowledgements

My grateful thanks go to my literary agent, James Essinger, who believed in me and in Lucy right from the start. To Richard Lester and John Waites for their reassuring proof reading. And to Charlotte Mouncey for her brilliant cover design and all her work on the book.

My special thanks go to my friends and family for all the love and support, but most especially to Kathy and Lindsay, for their unwavering friendship. And to Chris, for reading and for believing.

I've saved until last the most important person I need to thank: my son, Sam. Wise beyond his years and my little rock.